INTRODUCTIO

Dear Plan-A-Home Reader,

This book is the latest publication under the umbrella of Plan-A-Home Ireland Ltd. "Designs for the 21st Century" follows the same principle as our previous publication "Concepts for Irish Homes," sales of which have been phenomenal and has been hailed by far the best book of its type on the Irish market. The content of this book we feel is even better and is designed in the hope of giving you an insight into the possibilities of designing and constructing your new home.

Designs in this book offer a wide variety of ideas and styles, scale and materials. They marry together traditional forms which reflect an image at the centre of Irish culture generating the need for shelter and work, and a definite move away from that traditional form towards a more modern approach, addressing the needs of today's society.

In keeping with modern trends we have dedicated a section to alternative energy and energy conservation. This section is supplied by HMG Architects and CMG Architects and is a testimony to their commitment to keeping their clients fully informed. This is of extreme importance, as your new home is intended to service occupancy for the next five to ten decades, so it is important to consider high specification finishes which will last long into the future.

We have endeavoured to present our new publication in an easy to read format. A majority of the schemes have been illustrated onto pages with plans, perspectives and alternative views giving, in most cases a complete house type at each turn of the page. Please always bear in mind that the plans and images are merely suggestions and staff at HMG and CMG offices will gladly assist you in demonstrating how these plans can be changed to accommodate your needs better.

A number of the drawings within the book are available directly from Plan-A-Home, although the book is presented as a collection of ideas. For those of you wishing to avail of this service see details on the order form on page 159.

To reiterate, this publication is intended to guide you through the many options that are open to you with design and construction of your home. Hopefully the content will go some way towards helping you analyse what you really want to suit your personal requirements and site needs. There is an endless number of alternatives open to you and our sister companies HMG Architects and CMG Architects are there to provide a full architectural service to those wishing to maximise on their investment should it be domestic or commercial.

We hope you enjoy the contents of this new publication, "Designs for the 21st Century," and that it may help you in creating your new home.

Harold McGuinness
(Managing Director)

COPYRIGHT

An *Unauthorised* **Third** *Party* architect
will provide you with a **Second** *Rate Service* and
leave you requiring a **First** *Class Lawyer*.

Use of Designs and Copyright Infringement

The Designs contained in this publication are the sole property of Plan-A-Home.
It is illegal to use these designs in any form, either as illustrated or altered without the prior consent of Plan-A-Home.

Options for Obtaining Designs or Copyright

Option 1
Standard Plans

All illustrated designs can be ordered directly through Plan-A-Home.
Please refer to page 4 and the Order Form on pages 159 & 160.

Option 2
Custom Design

The general concept of any of the illustrated designs can be altered and re-worked to suit your personal requirements.

This service is provided through any of the HMG or CMG offices throughout thecountry, (see inside back cover).
This service can also be provided together with a full architectural package as outlined on pages 5, 6 & 7.

Option 3
Purchase of Copyright

In the event that you already have your own architect/agent who wishes to draw up your plans using a design concept illustrated in this book, you can obtain permission to do so through Plan-A-Home.
The fee for purchase of copyright will be based on a percentage of the purchase price of a set of working drawings.

Please ensure that you adhere to one of the two criteria outlined above when using any of the illustrated designs in any form.
Failure to comply with this has left us with no alternative but to prosecute those in breach of our copyright.
Remember - Houses cannot hide!

Copyright Note

ALL THE PLANS IN THIS BOOK ARE PROTECTED BY COPYRIGHT

CONTENTS

PUBLISHERS

Plan-A-Home
Lower Main Street,
Letterkenny, Co. Donegal.
www.plan-a-home.ie

BOOK MAKE UP & GRAPHICS

InCADessence

Office 8c, The Courtyard
Lower Main St.
Letterkenny, Co. Donegal.
Tel: (074) 9127842
Email: info@incadessence.com
Web Site: www.incadessence.com

PRINTERS

Universities Press
Alanbrooke Road,
Belfast.

ACKNOWLEDGEMENTS

Designs:
HMG Associates, Architects
CMG Associates, Architects

Editorials:
Patrick McCarthy - Gardens
HMG Associates - Interiors and Energy
CMG Associates - Interiors and Energy
Gina McGarvey - Interiors
Irish Energy Centre - Energy Guidelines
3DCafe - 3D cars and people

Graphics:
InCADessence - Computer Images, Paintings
3DCafe - 3D cars and people

A simple and economical means of obtaining high quality plans and contract specification. All plans are prepared to:

- a high quality of design and presentation;

- comply with current Building Regulations;

- include your own specific choices of materials and finishes.

TO ORDER YOUR PLANS

CALL 1890 222345
or 1850 222345
or 00 353 74 29651 (outside Eire)
and talk to one of our staff. You will be informed of the cost of your plans and how quickly you can expect to receive them.
THEN
FILL out the forms on pages
159 & 160
This service is ONLY available through PLAN-A-HOME.

FOR ON LINE ORDERING PLEASE VISIT
www.plan-a-home.ie

PLEASE ENSURE THAT YOUR CHOICE OF PLANS ARE MOST SUITED TO YOUR NEEDS. IF YOU ARE IN ANY DOUBT PLEASE CONTACT ANY OF THE HMG OR CMG OFFICES FOR A CONSULTATION. (SEE PAGE 5).

THE FULL ARCHITECTURAL SERVICE:
FOR CUSTOMISED DESIGNS

HMG Associates, Architects.   CMG Associates, Architects.

See inside back cover for office details and locations.

All of the following services are provided by **HMG Associates/CMG Associates** throughout Ireland, check inside rear cover for nearest office. These architects retain the sole franchise from PLAN-A-HOME to work and alter any Plan-A-Home design to suit client needs.

Site Analysis & Survey

This is most important in ascertaining the house style to best suit your site and needs. Design style, proper aspect, best views, creating best impression at entrance to site, relationship to adjoining structures, planning constraints are some of the many concerns, (see also pages 77 & 78). Other information in relation to preparation of site maps for planning and tendering is observed and recorded on site.

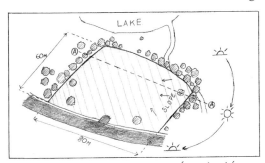

site survey

orientation

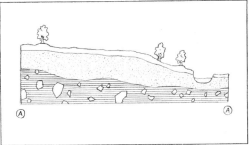

site section

Design Consultation

Comprehensive discussions are required to determine your needs in order to prepare the initial sketch layouts. You may wish to bring the following to any design meeting:
a personalised wish list; this should include initial design brief ideas, special requirements, budget and any other relevant material.
From here we can, in simple steps, work towards an agreed final design.

Planning   Permission

Preparations and submissions of all planning drawings and site layouts together with documents and notices required for planning applications. Liaison with the local planning authority should any difficulties arise during your application.

Working Drawings

After grant of Planning, the Planning Drawings are then advanced to Working drawings and specifications. These are to a standard that building contractors are fully aware of all details and finishes required, both for tendering and construction purposes, therefore eliminating unforeseen extras.

THE FULL ARCHITECTURAL SERVICE:
FOR CUSTOMISED DESIGNS

Tendering Procedures

A list of builders to tender is normally drawn up by agrement between the Architect and client. Tender analysis i.e. thorough scrutiny of tenders, is fundamental to the successful awarding of any contract.

Quantity Surveying

Prior to finalising any design we strongly recommend that you avail of our Quantity Surveying Service. This runs in parallel with our Architectural service to establish construction costs and to highlight any design adjustments necessary to suit specific budgets. Having your scheme costs in advance is very useful when evaluating tender and budgeting for interim payments.

Supervision

Supervision of any project is highly recommended as the unsuspecting client can easily be caught out by contractual loopholes and the unscrupulous builder.
Supervision involves constant liaison with contractors, client and other members of the design team to achieve the best results and make certain that all efforts expended during design are strictly enforced.
We ensure that all works and finishes are up to the highest standard and in compliance with Building Regulations, Planning and Mortgage Requirements.
In essence this service removes responsibility and liability for those who are in the process of building.

Structural Inspections

If full supervision is not required, structural inspections are advisable and indeed a prerequisite for most mortgage companies.
This involves:-
i) inspection of open foundation trenches.
ii) inspection of preparation of concrete ground floors.
iii) inspection of all roofing timbers and structures.
iv) inspection at practical completion.

* These services would be included within the full supervision package.

Housing Schemes

The Service includes:
Preliminary investigations, site suitability and analysis, full survey.
Design concepts for housing and site.
Working drawings, site layout, services drawings.

Bill of Quantities, relevant cost projections.
Tailored supervision requirements.
3-Dimensional computer modelling.
We offer a comprehensive service to potential developers.
Call into any of our offices to discuss your requirements. Office locations are given inside back cover.

THE FULL ARCHITECTURAL SERVICE:
Commercial and Industrial Design

Apartment Block, Cork.

Projects to date include:

Commercial - Hotels
Shopping Units
Office Developments
Apartment Blocks
Schools
Bars & Lounges
Restaurants
Marina Developments
Tourism Projects
Aircraft Hangars
Golf Clubs
Nursing Homes
Remedial Care Facilities
Filling Stations

Industrial - Business Park
Fish Processing Plants
Storage & Retail Units
Fish Handling Units
Light Industrial Facilities

Commercial/Industrial

With professional teams of architectural staff both **HMG Associates** and **CMG Associates** handle all types of projects, from design to planning, tendering and supervision. This service is backed up with state of the art computerised drawing offices offering both flexibility in design and photo-realistic images.

Proposed Business Park, Donegal.

Apartment Block and Public House Development, Cork.

INITIAL STEPS

The following is a list of important issues which you should ensure are in place before commencing construction on you new home:-

1.   CHOOSING YOUR SITE:

It is important to take into account that no two sites are alike and not all dwelling types are appropriate for every site.

It is necessary to make sure that your site can facilitate the many difficult aspects of the type of house you hope to build. Purchasers should be aware that buying a site 'outright', with outline planning permission only, does not necessarily guarantee them the type of house they may require.

The nature of the soil and site gradients are of the upmost importance when deciding on a site. Excessive filling or excessive excavation, can result in hefty expenditure. Also, soil types would be of such a nature as to require an effluent treatment system as opposed to traditional septic tanks. Percolation tests are more often than not required to accompany any planning application. Check with your architect / local authority for your county requirements. These tests, in many cases, will determine the means of effluent treatment required for your site.

Matters such as development cost, available services, and planning restrictions are all contentious issues and therefore you should seek the help of your Architect. It is possible to buy serviced sites from developers; this means that all drainage, water, electricity and other relevant services are provided onsite.

2.   CONVEYANCING:

Ensure that the legal conveyancing of your site has been completed thoroughly in regard to site boundaries, easements for access or services, and any liability towards common accesses, or services clearly defined and highlighted. Have your site boundaries checked independently to ensure that they comply with your transfer documents.

3.   MORTGAGING:

If you are arranging a mortgage this should be done before or in tandem with getting your house designs and permission so as to:-
(1) ensure that you can obtain sufficient funds to complete your home.
(2) Ensure that you comply with the many conditions laid down by your mortgage company in relation to structural checks, supervision.

4. HOUSE PLANS:

There are an infinite number of possibilities and issues involved in designing your dwelling. There will always be a number of compromises to be made between your desires and the possible constraints of the site itself coupled with planning restrictions. For instance, should you choose a plan from this book that you feel is perfect for you it may still need alterations to comply with the above requirements. This is the service that we at HMG and CMG specialise in, therefore it is always advisable to seek a consultation prior to finalising your house design. We can also assist and advise you on other anxieties you may have in regard to planning, assistance with tendering, construction issues, and supervision. This service ensures that all the initial efforts and discussions which resulted in your chosen plan being put on paper are instigated on site.

Spending worthwhile time in obtaining professional assistance at an early stage such as this inevitability saves a lot of time, problems and headaches that many encounter at a later date during construction.

5. PLANNING PERMISSION:

Full planning permission must be received before any work can commence. Ensure also that any statutory objection periods which may exist, have elapsed, and any conditions outlined on your planning permission, are complied with during construction. Any considerations outlined in your planning permission are incorporated into your building contract prior to tendering and complied with during construction.

6. BUILDING REGULATIONS:

All plans and specifications should be to Building Regulations standards, and passed by the relevant authorities if applicable in your area. Likewise, you should ensure that the contractor is fully conversant with the current Building Regulations, and fully intends to construct the dwelling in compliance with same.

7. COMMENCEMENT NOTICE:

In the Republic of Ireland you are currently obliged to submit a Commencement Notice stating your intention to commence work between fourteen and twenty-eight days. These forms can be obtained from your local authority.

8. INSURANCE:

Insurance cover is vital during the course of construction to protect your investment. This is especially important if you are building your dwelling on a self-build method as all too often clients forget, to their loss. If your house has been constructed under contract then ensure that your builder has a policy to cover for these eventualities. Insurance cover should cover for at least storm damage, fire damage, public and employers liability insurance, all risks.

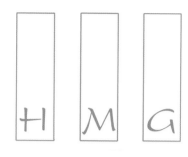

QS Division

Office 8b The Courtyard
Lower Main Street
Letterkenny
Co. Donegal
email: lkenny@hmg.ie
tel: 074 9127844
fax: 074 9127841

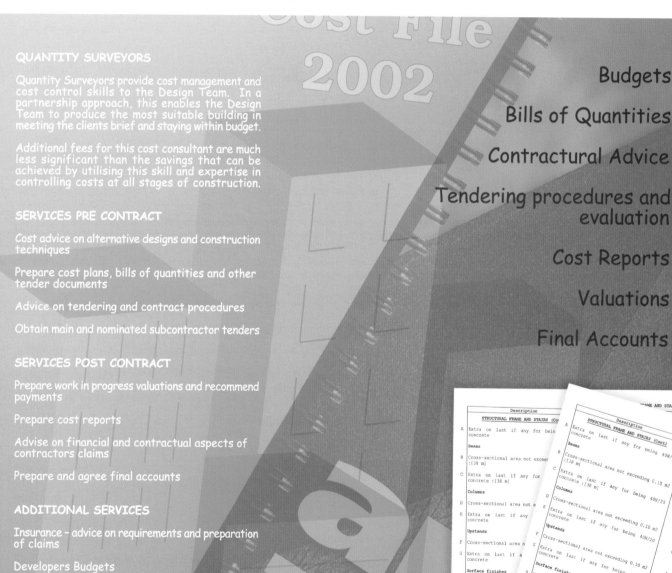

QUANTITY SURVEYORS

Quantity Surveyors provide cost management and cost control skills to the Design Team. In a partnership approach, this enables the Design Team to produce the most suitable building in meeting the clients brief and staying within budget.

Additional fees for this cost consultant are much less significant than the savings that can be achieved by utilising this skill and expertise in controlling costs at all stages of construction.

SERVICES PRE CONTRACT

Cost advice on alternative designs and construction techniques

Prepare cost plans, bills of quantities and other tender documents

Advice on tendering and contract procedures

Obtain main and nominated subcontractor tenders

SERVICES POST CONTRACT

Prepare work in progress valuations and recommend payments

Prepare cost reports

Advise on financial and contractual aspects of contractors claims

Prepare and agree final accounts

ADDITIONAL SERVICES

Insurance – advice on requirements and preparation of claims

Developers Budgets

Cost in use studies

Value engineering

Risk Management

Health and Safety advice

Budgets

Bills of Quantities

Contractural Advice

Tendering procedures and evaluation

Cost Reports

Valuations

Final Accounts

Quantity Surveyors   Construction Economists

SECTION A: DESIGNS 2001-2030
Floor Areas up to 1800 square feet

 Page12-2001

 Page13-2002

 Page14-2003

 Page15-2004

Page16-2005

Page18-2006

 Page24-2007

 Page26-2008

Page27-2009

Page28-2010

Page30-2011

Page31-2012

 Page32-2013

 Page40-2014

Page41-2015

Page42-2016

Page44-2017

Page45-2018

 Page48-2019

 Page49-2020

Page50-2021

Page51-2022

Page54-2023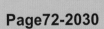

Page56-2024

 Page58-2025

Page60-2026

Page66-2027

Page68-2028

Page70-2029

Page72-2030

11

Front Perspective

2001

Two Bedrooms.
Living - 15' 10"x16' 05"
Kitchen\Dining - 12' 11"x16' 05"
Bed 1 - 11' 07"x16' 05"
Bed 2 -12' 11"x16' 05"
Overall Length - 42' 08"
Overall Width - 18' 06"
Floor Area - 1238 sq. ft.

Bed 1

HW

Bath

Bed 2

First Floor Plan

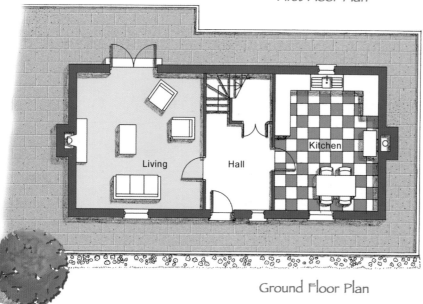

Living

Hall

Kitchen

This is a traditional one and a half storey house with raised plaster bands to windows, doors and corners. The kitchen is large enough to facilitate items normally planned for a utility room. The hall press could, however, be easily modified to create a utility space if desired. The two bedrooms are very spacious with Bed one benefiting from a walk-in-wardrobe.

Ground Floor Plan

For **Construction Costs**
See Pages 74 & 75

Copyright 2000 Plan-A-Home

View from front garden towards main entrance

This 3 bedroomed dwelling benefits from a clearly defined floor plan: sleeping accomodation is to the rear and private; the sitting room is at the front and public, and the living areas are grouped together on the other side of the hall.
Large front windows will provide plenty of natural light to the living quarters.

Floor Plan

2002

Three Bedrooms.
Overall Length - 49' 07''
Overall Width - 46' 09''
Sitting - 15' 9''x14' 09''
Living - 12' 6''x10' 06''
Kitchen\Dining - 12' 04''x20' 08''
Bed 1 - 15' 9''x10' 00''
Bed 2 -13' 00''x10' 10''
Bed 3 -9' 00''x10' 10''
Floor Area - 1528 sq. ft.

View from Drive Entrance

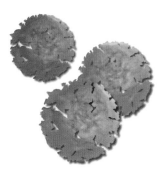

For Construction Costs
See Pages 74 & 75

Front Perspective

2003

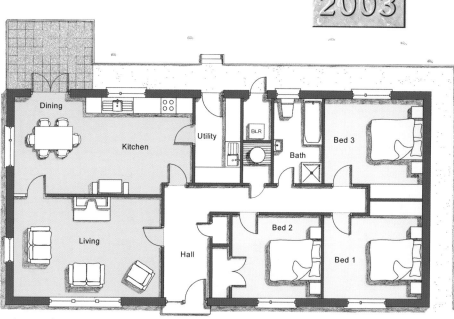

Dining

Kitchen

Utility

BLR

Bath

Bed 3

Living

Hall

Bed 2

Bed 1

Floor Plan

A modern style bungalow with full height windows to the large living room. The front door is fully glazed with a window to the side which will provide much light to the hall. An internal porch could be created by the addition of a door and screen in the same way as it is on Design 2004 - see page opposite.

Rear Perspective

Three Bedrooms.
Kitchen\Dining - 23' 00"x11' 11"
Living - 19' 00"x12' 04"
Bed 1 - 12' 08"x12' 02"
Bed 2 -11' 06"x10' 04"
Bed 3 - 12' 08"x12' 04"
Overall Length - 54' 08"
Overall Width - 26' 09"
Floor Area - 1302 sq. ft.

For **Construction Costs**
See Pages 74 & 75

Front   Perspective

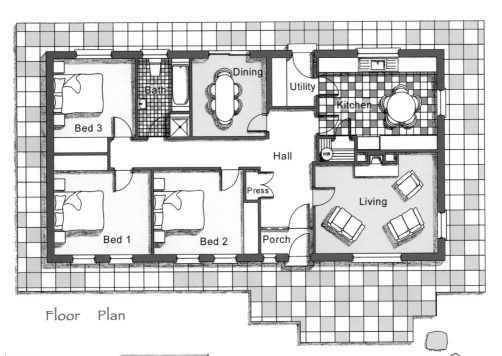

Floor   Plan

Three Bedrooms.
Kitchen - 16' 00"x11' 09"
Living - 16' 06"x12' 00"
Bed 1 - 13' 00"x11' 00"
Bed 2 -12' 00"x11' 00"
Bed 3 -11' 00"x10' 03"
Overall Length - 53' 07"
Overall Width - 27' 06"
Floor Area - 1321 sq. ft.

2004

Similar in many ways to the previous design but with a difference in fenestration. There are two smaller windows to each front bedroom instead of one large one.

This design benefits from a separate dining room, however, both houses have patio doors to their dining areas.

For **Construction Costs**
See Pages 74 & 75

Front Perspective

2005

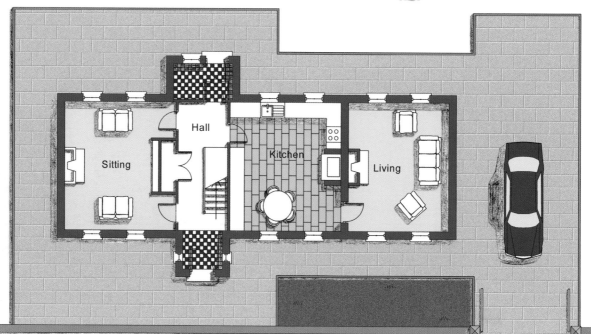

Sitting

Hall

Kitchen

Living

Ground Floor Plan

For **Construction Costs**
See Pages 74 & 75

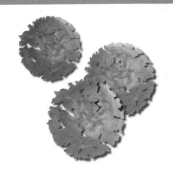

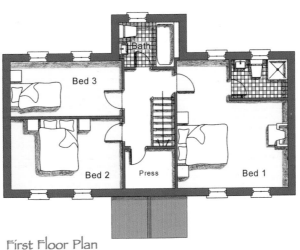

First Floor Plan

The same design ; mirrored and with a thatched roof

Three Bedrooms.
Kitchen\Dining - 14' 09"x16' 05"
Living - 14' 09"x16' 05"
Sitting - 14' 09"x16' 05"
Bed 1 - 14' 09"x16' 05"
Bed 2 -14' 09"x9' 00"
Bed 3 - 14' 09"x7' 01"
Overall Length - 52' 10"
Overall Width - 28' 03"
Floor Area - 1540 sq. ft.

As the main image but with a different colour finish

A traditional two storey house with a single storey addition.

This dwelling is only one room deep which allows those rooms to have a dual aspect, to both front and rear.

The main body of the house is symmetrical with a central porch and chimney stacks centred on the gable ends.

Many of the houses in this book can be finished equally successfully with different materials.

Here a thatched roof looks as good as a tiled one. Your decision could be based on personal preference or compliance with local planning requirements.

View towards front

Ideal for a rural setting with adequate kitchen/dining space and reasonable guest/family bedrooms, but the main thrust of this design is the exceptionally spacious living/sun lounge and master bedroom. The
Sun lounge could if wished be screened off from main living space to create a cosy winter space. This layout shows the option of an attractive spiral stair in a double height hallway.

Ground Floor Plan

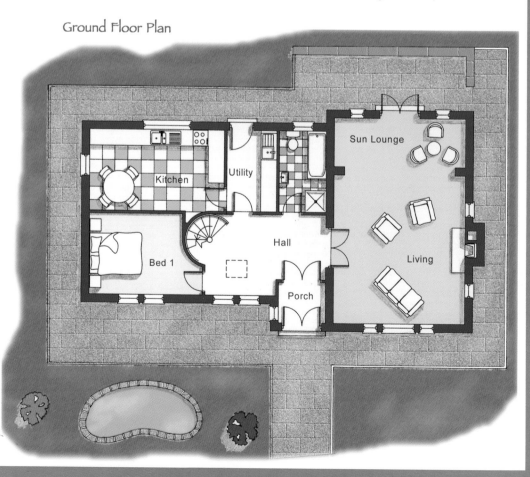

For **Construction Costs**
See Pages 74 & 75

18

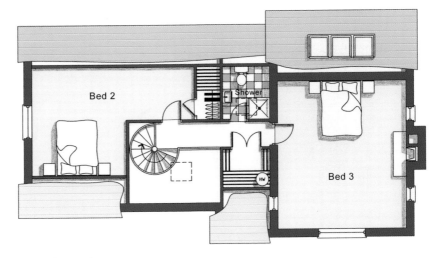

First Floor Plan

Three Bedrooms.
Living - 16' 05''x18' 01''
Kitchen - 17' 01''x9' 10''
Sun lounge - 16' 05''x6' 11''
Bed 1 - 14' 05''x9' 10''
Bed 2 -20' 04''x13' 02''
Bed 3 - 16' 05''x18' 01''
Overall Length - 50' 08''
Overall Width - 26' 11''
Floor Area - 1728 sq. ft.

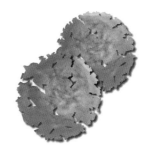

Interior Perspective of Living Room

HALLMARK WALLING
by

THE ALTERNATIVE TO NATURAL STONE OR BRICKWORK

The use of natural stone and brickwork has been with us for many centuries; its durability and aesthetic appeal ensures their continued use in modern day construction.

Natural stone is an expensive form of construction, often difficult to source and very labour intensive. It requires the skills of a stone mason, and must be hand picked to achieve the desired effect.

Roadstone with its policy of constant product innovation has developed the Hallmark range of walling, which is the ideal alternative to Natural stone, at a fraction of the cost and is seen by many as a welcome change for the all "too standard" clay brick. Hallmark Walling, unlike natural stone is available ex stock and can easily be laid by a bricklayer.

Hallmark can be built using different bond patterns including random bond, coursed bond and random brought to course, thus allowing the flexibility to give any house or housing development a unique appearance.

The success of Hallmark walling can be illustrated by its presence in almost every county throughout Ireland. It is particularly suited to areas where planning considerations call for extra sensitivity.

Private house, Co. Louth. *Pewter Colour*

Its ability to merge easily with beautiful surroundings or traditional architecture can contribute enormously to the local environment.

The use of contrasting coloured mortars combined with the seven different colours in the Hallmark range is a very important consideration, as this can have a significant effect on the overall appearance.

Joints can be finished flush, tooled or bagged depending on the overall effect required and local custom. Recessed joints are not recommended.

On a practical level it is built using standard cavity wall construction and can be easily combined with brickwork or render. This is beautifully illustrated below – Here Hallmark Pewter Blend in random bond is complemented by an Ormonde "Orchard Wall" clay brick in a private residence. This is just one of many beautiful examples of its use.

Private House. *Pewter Blend with Ormonde 'Orchard Wall' brick*

Detail. Co. Waterford

Brickwork or quoin stones in either smooth or a textured finish are available to compliment the range of colours. Although they are not necessary for the construction, they are an attractive feature and can enhance and add character to any house.

Hallmark walling is available nation-wide and is accompanied by a county-wide technical backup service for your convenience.

Why not call us for a full colour brochure to see for yourself the flexibility, versatility and beauty of Hallmark walling as used in a variety of projects which will convince you that Hallmark Walling is the modern day alternative to brickwork and expensive stonework.

EASY·FIX
GLASSBLOCKS

The **Easyfix** Glassblock system is ideal for any DIY enthusiast because of the simple and fast assembly process required for construction of glassblock panels.

The construction time is one fifth of the time of normal Glassblocks, allowing you to start and finish a panel in one go.

The unique PVC Collar system ensures uniformity in the joints.

The Easyfix Glassblocks come in a range of colours and patterns to add style and character to any application.

KIT COMPOSITION

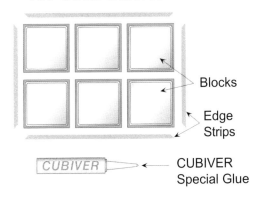

Blocks

Edge Strips

CUBIVER Special Glue

roadstone

Contact us at :
Roadstone Architectural Products Division,
Huntstown, North Road,
Finglas, Dublin 11
Phone 01-8343322   Fax   01-8343931
www.roadstone.ie

A Room with a View

Add space, value, comfort and class to your home with a sun lounge
– Made easy with a Keystone Lintel

A sun lounge offers:

- *Much better heat retention in winter*
- *Protection from the blazing summer sun*
- *Noise reduction such as that associated with rainfall on a glass roof*

The construction of a Sun Lounge has been simplified by the introduction of the **Keystone Sun Lounge Lintel**. This is a one piece unit which allows architects to design the Sun Lounge to suit the property, and will keep costs at a sensible level. The Keystone Sun Lounge Lintel is manufactured and delivered ready for erection.

Its as easy as...

DESIGNING FOR THE DISABLED

New Design Criteria

In order to ensure that all sections of society both able bodied and those with disabilities are catered for in the design of buildings, the architect must incorporate the recommendations set out in Part M of the Building Regulations. Recently Part M has been up dated so that designs would cater more readily for people with disabilities.

This revised document applies to all dwellings where works are commenced on or after 1st January 2001, except for new dwellings where planning has been applied for on or before 31st December 2000 and where substantial works are completed by 31st December 2003

As these designs in this new publication were prepared prior to the introduction of this up date of Part M, some of the designs may require alterations in order to accommodate the new recommendations. We have outlined below the main points of this document which may have an effect on our design.

The main aim of the Technical Guidance Document M is to "ensure that dwellings are visitable by people with disabilities".

Dwelling design should now ensure that:

1. People with disabilities can safely and conveniently approach and gain access.
2. People with disabilities have access to the main habitable rooms at entry level.
3. A W.C is provided at entry level on a storey containing the main living room with adequate provision for access.
4. A clear area of 1.2 m sq. should be provided at the entrance door.
5. A maximum threshold of 15mm to allow for easy access.
6. Door handles and lights are at an accessible level.

The points outlined above are only a brief extract from Part M from the current Building Regulations. When enquiring about any of our designs, our technicians will advise if that design requires alterations to comply with this section of the Building Regulations.

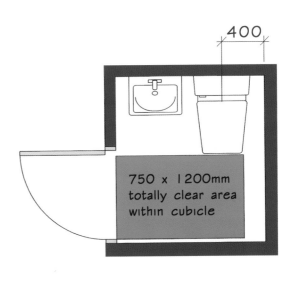

400

750 x 1200mm totally clear area within cubicle

400

750 x 1200mm totally clear area within cubicle

View to front of house

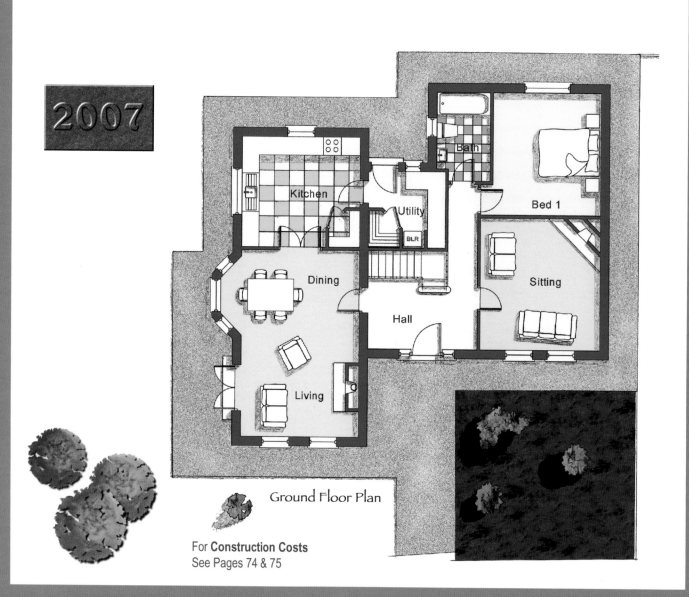

2007

Ground Floor Plan

For **Construction Costs**
See Pages 74 & 75

Three Bedrooms.
Living\Dining - 13' 01"x20' 00"
Kitchen - 13' 01"x11' 09"
Sitting - 13' 01"x14' 01"
Bed 1 - 11' 10"x13' 01"
Bed 2 -11' 08"x11' 06"
Bed 3 - 13' 01"x11' 10"
Overall Length - 44' 00"
Overall Width - 39' 01"
Floor Area - 1520 sq. ft.

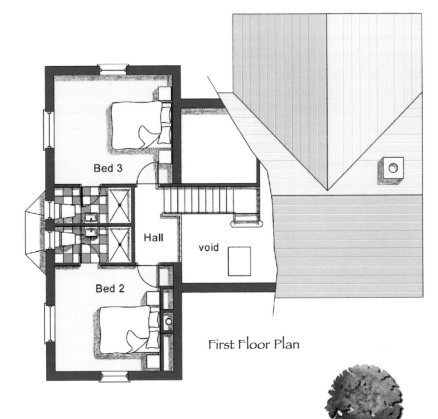

First Floor Plan

This design suggests the idea of providing the main dining area within the living space. A spacious double high lobby gives an elegant feeling with an overlooking landing leading to two en-suite rooms.

View towards rear with dining room bay to right

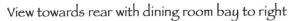

25

Front Perspective

A practical starter home complete with en-suite, rear w.c. and separate utility. The kitchen/dining is adequate to back up as a general living area and the overall arrangement of the room should be carefully thought out if this is the intention. This hand of design is suited to a southerly aspect.

Three Bedrooms.
Kitchen/Dining - 13' 02"x18' 10"
Living - 15' 08"x12' 03"
Bed 1 - 12' 06"x12' 03"
Bed 2 -13' 07"x9' 10"
Bed 3 - 9' 06"x9' 10"
Overall Length - 49' 03"
Overall Width - 28' 04"
Floor Area - 1259 sq. ft.

2008

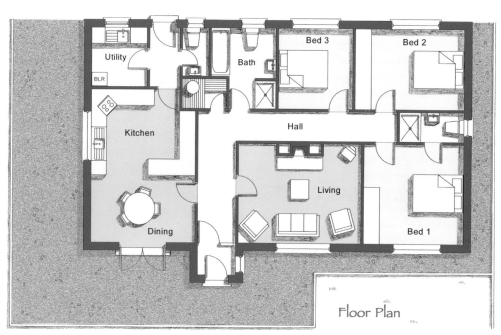

Floor Plan

For **Construction Costs**
See Pages 74 & 75

View from drive towards front

An economical use of space with four bedrooms including en-suite, utility and W.C. The link hall between rear and main hall may in some cases be unnecessary with the space better utilized in the kitchen. Similarities are drawn with design 2018.

Floor Plan

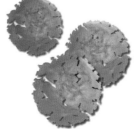

Four Bedrooms.
Kitchen/Dining - 13' 07''x12' 08''
Living - 16' 03''x12' 03''
Bed 1 - 13' 01''x10' 07''
Bed 2 -11' 06''x10' 07''
Bed 3 - 13' 01''x10' 06''
Bed 4 - 13' 01''x8' 06''
Overall Length - 49' 01''
Overall Width - 38' 06''
Floor Area - 1323 sq. ft.

For **Construction Costs**
See Pages 74 & 75

View from drive towards living room bay and main entrance

2010

Two Bedrooms.
Living - 15' 09''x12' 06''
Kitchen\Dining - 20' 08''x12' 00''
Sitting - 14' 11''x13' 00''
Bed 1 - 14' 08''x12' 06''
Bed 2 -13' 01''x12' 06''
Overall Length - 40' 04''
Overall Width - 30' 00''
Floor Area - 1484 sq. ft.

Bed 2

Bath

Hall

Bed 1

First Floor Plan

For **Construction Costs**
See Pages 74 & 75

Ground Floor Plan

See how well some houses are better suited to stone than others, the proportions and style of this house regardless of where you view it from, speaks for itself. The style and entrance locations make this especially suited to a narrow or confined site if necessary. A wide, airy hall surrounded by living quarters and leading onto a landing with two spacious bedroom. The utility door could be repositioned giving more space to W.C. for disabled access.

View of front showing stone finish

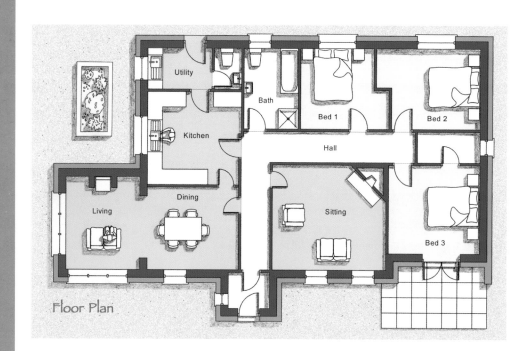

Floor Plan

Three Bedrooms.
Overall Length - 58' 03''
Overall Width - 31' 08''
Living - 9' 10''x12' 00''
Dining - 12' 01''x10' 07''
Sitting - 15' 02''x13' 05''
Kitchen - 12' 05''x11' 11''
Bed 1 - 11' 10''x10' 04''
Bed 2 -13' 07''x10' 04''
Bed 3 -12' 00''x11' 04''
Floor Area - 1383 sq. ft.

The same design but with a Rendered Finish

For **Construction Costs**
See Pages 74 & 75

A popular choice with very well appointed kitchen/living areas availing of maximum natural light. The external façade is traditional and exceptionally appealing. If preferred the entrance hall could be eliminated giving more space to the living area.

Front   Perspective

Another traditional design this time with a symmetrical facade; a pleasing feature of which is the two bay windows within the end gables.

The sitting\dining room has windows to three walls so proper site orientation will provide a sunny aspect for most of the day.

2012

Three Bedrooms.
Kitchen - 9' 02"x14' 01"
Living\Dining - 12' 06"x19' 08"
Bed 1 - 10' 01"x8' 10"
Bed 2 -11' 06"x10' 08"
Bed 3 -11' 06"x10' 08"
Overall Length - 61' 08"
Overall Width - 25' 02"
Floor Area - 1150 sq. ft.

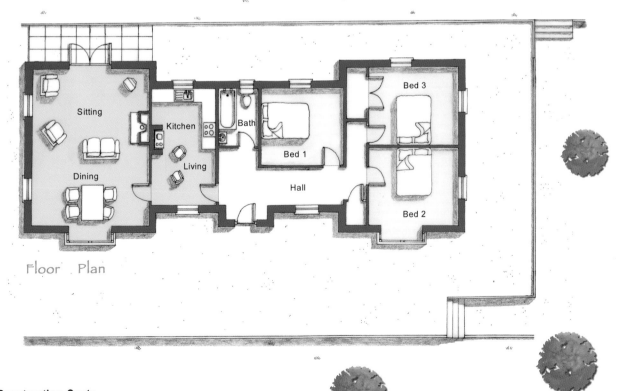

Floor Plan

For Construction Costs
See Pages 74 &75

View from garden with study on left and sun lounge on right

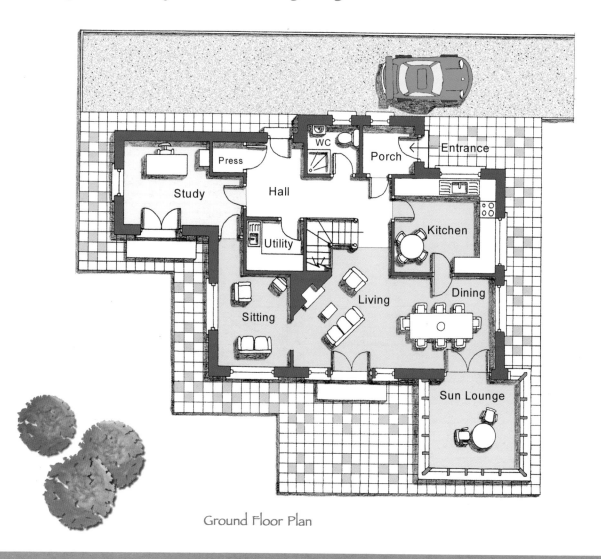

Ground Floor Plan

For **Construction Costs**
See Pages 74 & 75

Three Bedrooms.
Living\Dining - 21' 00"x9' 00"
Kitchen - 10' 06"x9' 00"
Sitting - 9' 00"x9' 00"
Sun lounge - 9' 00"x9' 00"
Study - 12 06"x8' 02"
Bed 1 - 8' 10"x8' 10"
Bed 2 -8' 10"x9' 00"
Bed 3 - 7' 7"x13' 06"
Overall Length - 43' 04"
Overall Width - 35' 09"
Floor Area - 1336 sq. ft.

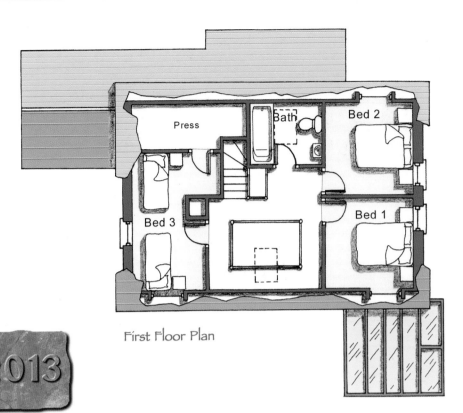

First Floor Plan

This plan allows for the formal separation of the office and the house. The living, kitchen and sitting areas are arranged in an open plan layout articulated by pinch points and a separate sun lounge area. The above has to be achieved in an essentially rectangular cube.

View from drive towards front door with sun lounge on left

33

CREATING AN ENTRANCE

First impressions are crucial. The entrance, being the first experience of a house often generates an image of the house as a whole. Traditionally the larger the house the grander the doorway, giving increased emphasis to the entrance.

The doorway itself is important; a heavy door will create a sense of solidity whilst a partially or fully glazed door will give a feeling of openness and light.

The front doors of Ireland traditionally made a statement. Finished with a bright primary colour such as red or blue, they contrast boldly with the whitewashed walls.

When choosing a door be true to the building, avoid bevelled glass, columns and pressed woodgrain on metal or upvc, all look inauthentic. A simple hardwearing timber door such as oak, elm or teak looks far better than a door pretending to have been crafted 100 years ago.

HALLWAYS AND PORCHES

One of the main functions of a hall is to create an area between inside and out and provide a means of circulation to and from different areas within the house. As an entrance to your home it must be accessible to all users and visitors including parents with prams and people in wheelchairs.

In the smaller house getting rid of the entrance hall to enlarge the living area may seem a good idea, but stepping directly into the living room deprives the occupant of the opportunity to shake off the outside prior to entering proper into a house.

For smaller houses it is best to leave a hallway uncluttered with storage provided for coats and shoes. Even coat hooks, when fully loaded on a wall will give the space a claustrophobic feel. The halfway point of a house is removed as a stranger at the door steps instantly into the heart of the home. A hallway acts as a breathing space and should be lit naturally wherever possible, creating a welcoming light warm area into which one feels comfortable in entering.

STAIRS

A staircase can generate one of the most dramatic focal points and should be treated as an active element within the house. It is the first thing visitors to the house see and is so often a missed opportunity. More and more, a staircase is adding to the status of a property and with the enormous choice of materials now available, from traditional timber to contemporary steel and glass it is easy to create an image suited to the individual.

Whichever treatment you choose the level of lighting is important. Low levels of light are acceptable and safe providing there is a clear distinction between the risers and treads. Avoid spotlights shining into people's eyes and flat shadowless light, both reduce the definition of the risers.

By introducing views and windows along the flight the journey up and down can be made more enjoyable. Using the walls for hanging paintings and photographs all help to give the staircase a sense of place.

KITCHENS

The kitchen is one of the most important centres of a house. It is not just a functional workspace but an area in which a family can live and interact.

Courtesy: Creative Wood Kitchens

An ever increasing interest in the kitchen as a family room has seen the re-emergence of the traditional kitchen as more open plan and incorporating a range and hearth.

When designing your own home the kitchen can be formulated to exact individual requirements. One of the most important steps is to decide what type of room and style of kitchen is required. If the kitchen is to be used as a social space it may be worthwhile spending time and money generating the correct spatial quality and light. Incorporating the dining room into the kitchen area can create an extra multi-functional space allowing interaction between working in the kitchen and activities within the adjoining space.

Careful planning of the kitchen is paramount to its success and ease of use. Everyone has their own individual requirements and priorities for kitchen design. There are however three primary functions; the washing area, the cooking area and the food storage. These will generate the fundamental layout of the kitchen. The relationship between these three functions is known as the work triangle, an imaginary line drawn between the three work centres. Each area must be clearly defined with clear passage from one area to another. The travel distances between the functions should be close enough as to not cause irritation from long travelling distances and far enough apart to avoid cramped movement.

Traditionally the sink was positioned in front of the window. It made sense to locate a function that can be time consuming next to a natural light source. This is not compulsory although it can feel odd facing a wall while using the sink. If a source of natural light is not available a more acceptable location would be facing out towards the room on an island or an outshot. Quality design is as much to do with being aesthetically pleasing as ensuring smooth performance.

With the amount of electrical appliances available it is easy to overload a kitchen with gadgets. All fitted appliances should be integrated into the overall design theme selected for the kitchen.

UTILITIES

With the advent of the utility room there is now a choice of location for the more bulky, noisy and visually unappealing items which would have normally been accommodated within the main kitchen area using up valuable storage space.

Offering a separate area where clothes can be washed, dried and ironed and all household cleaning equipment can be stored reinforces the identity of the kitchen as an integral part of the house. The utility acts as a rear porch from the outside keeping dirt and wet away from the kitchen. It offers the opportunity to remove coats and shoes before entering the main house.

A utility room should have easy clean surfaces for the floor, walls and units, a double or deep sink unit for handwashing clothes and space for the washing machine and tumble dryer.

A drying rack either floor or ceiling mounted is a necessary accessory even if a tumble dryer is installed. A ceiling rack will save space.

The utility room is also an ideal location for boiler, freezers, the hot-press and the storage of household products such as shoe cleaning equipment and general household products. It is also the ideal location for a w.c. so eliminating the need to remove shoes or coats prior to entering the house.

Courtesy: Creative Wood Kitchens

DINING ROOMS

Eating should be a social activity and not just a re-fuelling process; A relaxing occasion in a pleasant atmosphere.

The traditional "formal" dining room has lost popularity just as the kitchen has an ever-increasing positive focus. Unless you formally entertain on a regular basis a formal room designated purely for dining will be a waste of a room receiving only occasional usage.

Today's dining room is a multi-functional space located ideally adjacent to the kitchen, in order to move food with ease between the two rooms. If the dining area is for entertaining purposes then a location close to the living room opens up a linking of social functions, passing easily from relaxing to eating without loosing the congenial mood.

A dining room has to be accessible throughout the day, with differing emphasis being placed on different meals with breakfast, lunch or the evening meal being the family focus.

The lighting of the room is essential, natural daylight gives a warm welcoming airy feel, ideal for breakfast and lunch. Whereas the subtle use of low lighting creates an intimate feel. Lighting is required to define space and create ambience.

Traditionally a low light centrally located would reinforce the table as the focus of the room. Today modern lighting directed at the table offers the same result.

Locating the dining room on the western side of the house allows the evening sunlight to be filtered into the room. Introducing french doors or a patio area creates a link with outside and provides a natural link with the garden for barbecues.

The dining room doubles as a study, a games room, an office and a playroom. In fact it can take on a variety of roles during the evolution of a family unit. With a large family, the extra room becomes essential with the potential of varying activities that will occur throughout the house making it one of the house most useful rooms.

For a small house the use of a combined kitchen dining area offers a more practical solution although it is important to demarcate the cooking and dining areas. A simple change in floor finish, using timber for the dining and tiles in the kitchen will give the desired separation. The use of a split level, practically separating the two spaces will give individual identity to both kitchen and dining. It is important however to treat each area sensitively with lighting and finishes to suit both functions.

When an eating room is part of the kitchen it may require isolation. The provision of waist high kitchen or storage units will define the areas and provide storage and worktop facilities at the same time. Decorative screens can be used to enclose the eating area for special occasions.

The ideal eating room could double as a playroom, study or gallery. It could be a lobby room or a sun trap for plants. The functional aspects should not restrict the imagination. A successful dining room can show flair and imagination.

LIVING ROOMS AND LOUNGES

These rooms are variously referred to as parlours, drawing rooms, dens, sitting rooms, and so on. The variety of names reflects the range of design approaches possible, but all refer to areas that are, essentially, gathering spaces in the home.

A comfortable living-room where you can sit back and relax, letting the worries of the day ebb away, is an essential part of any home and can play a major role in the social life within the dwelling. On the other hand, it can be that room within a home which may simply be a private refuge or den away from the hustle often associated with the kitchen/general living areas. It can also take the shape of a more formal lounge along the lines of the old parlour or "good room" - seldom used except on those rare occasions when visitors called and, of course, at Christmas. The parlour was a room which always created an impression on the people who frequented it, from the child who was rarely allowed within its hallowed walls to the adult who remembers the atmosphere and essence of the parlour of their youth with a nostalgia, and with a longing to recreate that place within their new home.

Whether there are one, two or even three of these rooms within a dwelling will largely depend on your own individual requirements and lifestyle, and on the needs of family and children. Your own intuition is vital in getting the design right. While on a practical level a design can be tested for its workability, there is no such easy solution to knowing if it will come to life for you. Many people feel that their ideas and feelings stem from an emotional or whimsical basis and that they cannot be practically justified, and so can often dismiss them as too personal to be relevant to discussions regarding their new home.

The client's intuition can provide the architect with guidelines, particularly in answer to the all-important question: *What makes you feel comfortable?* It may be light, open spaces, a view, internal features or maybe well-defined rooms. Hence, it is good to throw out all your ideas for discussion. Then they can be looked at from all points of view such as design, workability and, of course, the ever-important but often forgotten budget.

The living-room, as with all rooms and their relationships are constantly changing both in size and role - shedding old ones and adopting new. While privacy is important and separate rooms such as bedrooms and bathrooms are still needed, the opening up of the living areas can be considered and has become increasingly popular with a move away from the clearly defined specific-use rooms like the parlour of former times. This is often achieved by combining rooms such as lounge/living/kitchen/dining into an all-encompassing open plan living area as is popular in many European countries. The space can be portioned out so that several people can happily share these areas while engaged in different activities. Nooks and crannies can be created with the overall space if so desired. Often the boundaries of the individual spaces can be delineated by the specific placement of furniture, change in level, variation of floor covering or possibly the introduction of vertical columns, bookshelves etc. Alternatively and possibly the most common today in Ireland - particularly since the kitchen has regained its position as the focus of the home - is the kitchen/dining/living room with the more formal lounge accessed off this area - possibly through a glazed screen or doors. This allows the rooms to be used individually where one can enjoy the luxury of a leisurely Sunday morning cup of coffee with a stack of papers or a good book while life goes on roundabout.

Alternatively, both rooms may be opened up for a function or gathering of people where an evening can progress from cooking to eating and on to relaxing in the lounge area.

In planning a lounge or living room one needs to be careful when deciding on the overall size and scale. Often, if moving from an existing dwelling where the room in question was too small, there can be a tendency to overcompensate in the proposed dwelling. The room should be large enough to carry out its function but not so large (and this applies particularly to a family room) that it loses its character and cosiness.

Where a large formal lounge is required it is often possible to incorporate a dining area within the room. This can be located on a different level or possibly within a projection bay. The need for a formal and separate dining room can then be eliminated giving maximum space to the lounge when needed.

The location of the living room and lounge (if separate rooms) would normally be such that their is a natural progression of sunlight from easterly morning sun in the kitchen through to the general living area during the day with the setting sun in the living area/lounge i.e. evening room. Having said this, however, where one's lifestyle is such that little if any time is spent in the kitchen area in the morning this may be altered to include sunlight to the kitchen/living area in the evening. This is a very personal and important decision and one where the in-tuition mentioned earlier has to be utilized.

The views, if one is lucky enough to have them, are also very important. It is generally felt that the view should be given to those rooms which get most use during the daytime hours such as kitchens and living rooms. Beware, however, not to sacrifice the light in favour of view. Though this is not a priority for everybody, most people will find that while a view is uplifting and there to be appreciated, it is generally a background feature of which one is only sporadically aware, while the presence of sunlight in the rooms in which most of the day is spent is of vital importance.

When all is said and done often it will be those last touches which will bring the rooms to life and instill character in them. This may be the paint colour, floor covering or perhaps a piece of personal furniture or a beautiful fireplace adorning the focal point of the room - possibly the last bastion of nostalgia in these centrally heated times.

Front perspective

Three Bedrooms.
Kitchen - 12' 05"x14' 02"
Living - 14' 06"x11' 06"
Sitting - 16' 00"x11' 06"
Bed 1 - 14' 06"x11' 10"
Bed 2 -9' 04"x10' 00"
Bed 3 -8' 02"x13' 10"
Overall Length - 53' 05"
Overall Width - 27' 11"
Floor Area - 1353 sq. ft.

The arched window pane facade is an optional feature for this popular design layout with 2 spacious bedrooms and a third medium double room. The practically laid out kitchen is complimented by an adequate and servicable utility. The 2 living rooms are both accessed off the main hall and deliberately kept separate for privacy reasons. Floor area could easily be adjusted to avail of house grant when required.

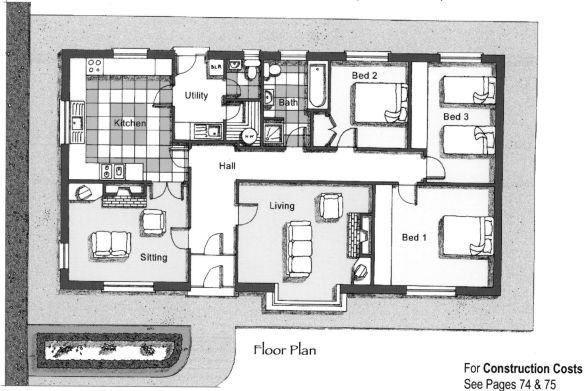

Floor Plan

For **Construction Costs**
See Pages 74 & 75

40

View of front

2015

Three Bedrooms.
Overall Length - 44' 03"
Overall Width - 27' 04"
Living - 12' 06"x12' 07"
Kitchen - 13' 08"x11' 09"
Dining - 13' 08"x9' 04"
Bed 1 - 10' 00"x13' 01"
Bed 2 - 10' 00"x11' 11"
Bed 3 - 9' 06"x8' 06"
Floor Area - 1076 sq. ft.

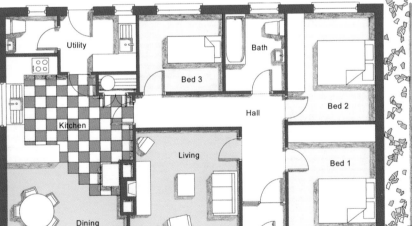
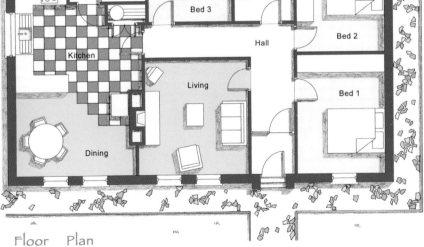

Utility

Bath

Bed 3

Bed 2

Hall

Kitchen

Living

Bed 1

Dining

Floor Plan

Designed with economy in mind and suited especially to those who prefer an open, spacious kitchen cum living area. The traditional barge and vertical window emphasis give it an appealing traditional rural appearance.

For **Construction Costs**
See Pages 74 & 75

41

View from front towards main entrance

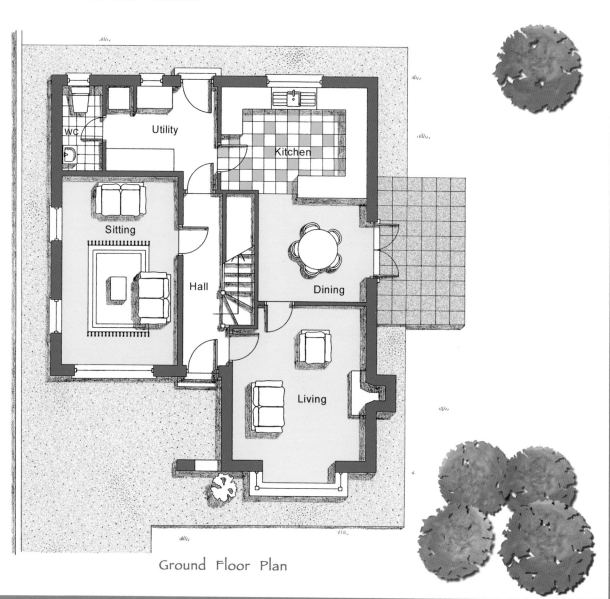

Ground Floor Plan

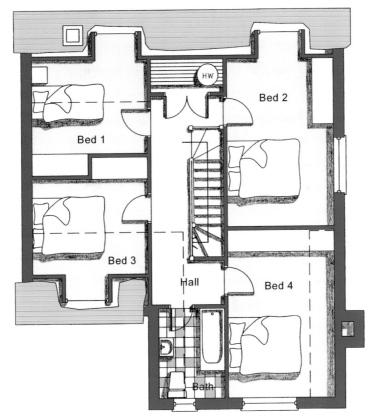

First Floor Plan

2016

An appealing dormer giving generous space to all rooms yet keeping floor area to a minimum by minimizing circulation area. Both floors have an easy free flowing arrangement with the scaled furniture illustrating room sizes. All Plan A Home designs can be altered to specific needs and in this case an en-suite may be desirable. The layout hand shown is suited to a north or west facing site and is ideal for a narrow frontage site.

Four Bedrooms.
Kitchen - 13' 03"x9' 11"
Dining - 9' 10"x9' 02"
Living - 12' 02"x13' 11"
Sitting - 10' 08"x16' 10"
Bed 1 - 10' 08"x8' 04"
Bed 2 - 9' 10"x15' 00"
Bed 3 - 10' 08"x8' 06"
Bed 4 - 9' 10"x14' 11"
Overall Length - 29' 10"
Overall Width - 37' 03"
Floor Area - 1550 sq. ft.

View from front left towards living room bay

Copyright 2000 Plan-A-Home

For **Construction Costs**
See Pages 74 & 75

43

Front Perspective

Maximum space afforded to living room and kitchen which is also intended for family living space. The angled doors to living room give a greater feeling of space to the main hall and again the scaled furniture to all rooms show all rooms to be adequately sized. The façade shows wide windows and conventional roof or could be rearranged using barges and narrow windows, like design 2019. Suited to a south facing site.

Three Bedrooms.
Kitchen/Dining - 16' 11"x15' 05"
Living - 14' 01"x15' 01"
Bed 1 - 11' 06"x13' 01"
Bed 2 -11' 06"x13' 07"
Bed 3 - 9' 08"x11' 02"
Overall Length - 51' 06"
Overall Width - 28' 10"
Floor Area - 1377 sq. ft.

2017

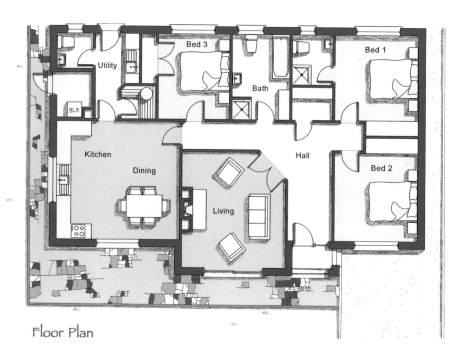

Floor Plan

For Construction Costs
See Pages 74 & 75

View from Site Entrance

For **Construction Costs**
See Pages 74 & 75

A design based on the same inter constraints as design 2017 only requiring an extra bedroom with-in the same square footage which slightly reduce living space. The traditional barge is optional and this hand of layout is best suited to a site facing west.

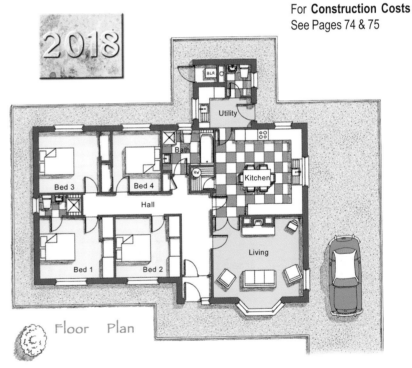

Floor Plan

Four Bedrooms.
Overall Length - 49' 01''
Overall Width - 44' 02''
Living - 16' 03''x13' 11''
Kitchen - 15' 07''x14' 09''
Bed 1 - 13' 01''x10' 07''
Bed 2 -11' 06''x10' 07''
Bed 3 - 12' 10''x10' 06''
Bed 4 - 8' 06''x10' 06''
Floor Area - 1367 sq. ft.

Side view towards living room and kitchen

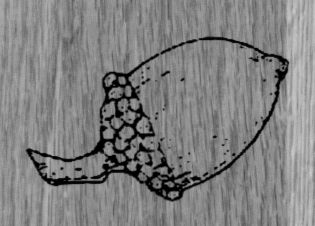

View from front left

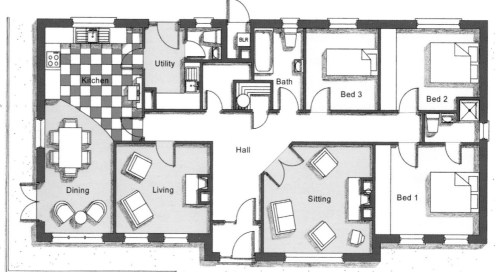

Floor Plan

Three Bedrooms.
Overall Length - 57' 08"
Overall Width - 29' 07"
Dining - 8' 10"x13' 06"
Living - 12' 00"x11' 01"
Kitchen - 12' 06"x11' 09"
Sitting - 14' 11"x13' 00"
Bed 1 - 12' 04"x11' 00"
Bed 2 -13' 00"x10' 01"
Bed 3 - 8' 10"x10' 01"
Floor Area - 1453 sq. ft.

View from driveway

This design hinges on the close integration of the kitchen, dining and living area on a southerly aspect site. As in many bungalows, provision can be made for future attic conversion but stair location should be well thought out at initial design stage. The chosen traditional appearance give the design a very distinctive appeal.

View from garden towards living and dining rooms

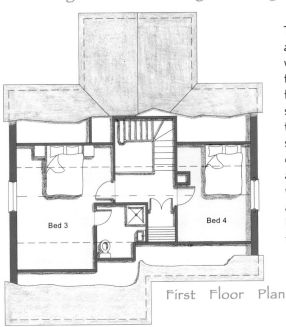

First Floor Plan

Bed 3

Bed 4

The design was formulated to accommodate a narrow site and vehicular parking near the rear, therefore entrance to main hall from the rear was the best solution yet providing an option to enter from front through a small reception porch. The main entrance proves very practical as guests arrive in the main hall, which in this case has an attractive staircase with both landing and entrance lighted from roof windows.

Four Bedrooms.
Kitchen/Dining - 15' 11"x17' 04"
Living - 16' 05"x11' 06"
Bed 1 - 10' 00"x10' 11"
Bed 2 -10' 02"x11' 02"
Bed 3 - 10' 02"x13' 00"
Bed 4 - 10' 10"x16' 07"
Overall Length - 34' 07"
Overall Width - 40' 04"
Floor Area - 1488 sq. ft.

Alternative material finishes

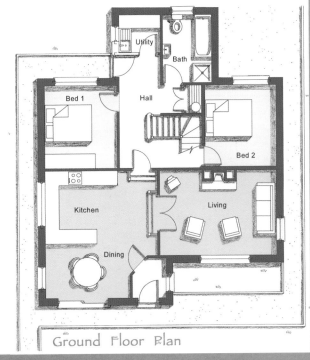

Ground Floor Plan

Front view towards living room bay

Three Bedrooms.
Kitchen - 10' 10''x14' 07''
Dining - 14' 09''x10' 09''
Living - 15' 09''x19' 04''
Sitting - 12' 05''x9' 06''
Bed 1 - 13' 05''x13' 06''
Bed 2 -11' 09''x11' 09''
Bed 3 -10' 06''x11' 05''
Overall Length - 64' 07''
Overall Width - 37' 07''
Floor Area - 1783 sq. ft.

For **Construction Costs**
See Pages 74 & 75

Floor Plan

Rear view towards entrance

2021

An extremely elegant house with a series of split levels to enhance the hall and living spaces. The house is specifically suited to a site which (a) has its entrance on the northern side and declines from the site entrance, and (b) requires the living quarters to be located to the rear due to sunlight and view. Therefore, the main entrance is at the opposite side to the living quarters, which in this case is practical and efficient.

Main view. The patio doors within the gable wall lead into the kitchen\dining area.

For **Construction Costs**
See Pages 74 & 75

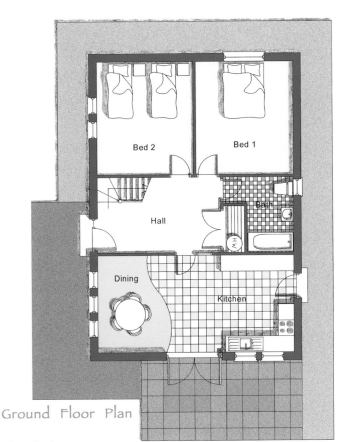

Ground Floor Plan

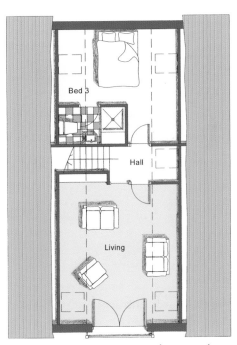

First Floor Plan

2022

Three Bedrooms.
Kitchen\Dining - 24' 06"x11' 09"
Living - 14' 10"x17' 05"
Bed 1 - 12' 01"x13' 09"
Bed 2 -12' 01"x13' 09"
Bed 3 - 14' 09"x13' 09"
Overall Length - 26' 05"
Overall Width - 36' 05"
Floor Area - 1345 sq. ft.

This design provides adequate open plan kitchen/living space on ground floor with a first floor living room to avail of views. The simplicity of the structure and roof together with use of roof windows in lieu of dormers ensures maximum economy.

51

What to Consider When Wiring Your New Home

Given most of us have to work within a budget, one of the major decisions facing most people building their own home is what to include at the building stage and what to leave until after they have moved in. Cabling, for example, is definitely one of those services that you really need to install at the construction stage.

Traditional Wiring now outdated in modern homes as technology advances

As more and more advanced technologies are now being made available within the home, the truth is that the traditional way of wiring homes is now no longer suitable. Services have changed dramatically over the past 20 years but the way houses are wired has not. In the past, homes typically had one telephone line, the TV service consisted of one aerial, there was no Internet in homes and a data network wasn't even a consideration. Today, however, homes may have numerous incoming telephone lines, including ISDN or Broadband, TV distribution has grown to incorporate cable TV and satellite, Video, DVD and CCTV cameras. New and emerging entertainment services such as digital TV, Surround sound, multi-room audio systems, home theatre systems and Plasma screens are gaining popularity among many home owners. Data networking is increasingly becoming a necessity for those wishing to connect multiple PC's for sharing of printers etc. There has also been a dramatic increase in the use of the Internet in the home.

Small Home Office

Home based working and small home offices are now on the increase as a result of increased travel times and traffic congestion in major towns and cities.

Broadband

Most new homes are currently being built without the cabling infrastructure in place to deal with Broadband. The arrival of the Broadband service to individual homes is like a Motorway arriving at a country lane. The infrastructure simply doesn't exist for the last 100 meters of the information highway.

Central Connection Centre

A Central Cabling System, which is installed in new homes at construction phase provides for the orderly management of cables throughout the home. Unlike the traditional adhoc way of cabling, ordinary cheap phone wire is not used nor are cables pulled in a loop around the homes. Instead only high quality and high speed cables are used and each socket is individually wired back to a Central Connection Centre. Incoming services such as Phone, TV, ISDN / Broadband etc are brought to this Central Connection Centre, typically located in the utility area, and from there they are distributed to every room in the home.

The importance of the cables

Many people think that because cable is buried in the wall and out of sight, it doesn't matter what cable you use. This is definitely not the case. The Cables are what carries all the various signals throughout your home and it is therefore the most important part to get right. There is also a benefit in using special multi-core cables where a number of cables are bundled together. This increases the access to services around the home while offering protection to cables as they are installed.

Preparing for the future now

With communications technology advancing at an ever increasing rate, it is logical to cable with future possibilities in mind. It just does not make sense to see the all-too-familiar picture of cables running across floors, tacked to skirting boards or draped across fireplaces in new homes.

There are many things you can change in your new home once you have moved in but wiring is not one of these. You only get one chance to wire a new home and you have to get it right, not only for now but also for the future.

*smart*homes

WIRING HOMES FOR THE FUTURE

NEW CENTRAL CABLING SYSTEM
AS SEEN ON DUNCAN STEWART'S TV SHOW "ABOUT THE HOUSE"

SMARTHOMES DESIGN, SUPPLY AND INSTALL CENTRAL CABLING SYSTEMS FOR .

- TV, Sky, Video
- DVD & Surround Sound
- Multi-room Internet Access
- Computers / Networking

- ISDN / Broadband Internet
- Plasma and Home Theatre
- Multi-room Audio
- Small Home Office

- CCTV Security Cameras
- Door / Gate Access
- Satellite Broadband
- Telephones

1 PLANNING AND DESIGN

- Expert Advice on choosing the best locations for your services e.g. Digital TV's, Speakers, Internet.
- Cabling Plan designed specifically for your home.

2 SMART CABLES

- High Speed, High Specification cables.
- Colour coded and Multi-core e.g. **Smart Orange** *Cable* contains separate cables for TV (Digital), High Speed Internet, Phone and an extra cable for future interactive services.
- These cables must be installed at the construction stage.

3 SMART CONNECTION CENTRE

- All cables are neatly organised in one Central connection centre, allowing for the integration, control and future upgrading of services.
- All incoming services e.g. Phone, TV (Digital), Internet are brought to this point, where they are effectively distributed to all sockets throughout the home.

4 SMART SOCKETS

- **Smart** Sockets allow you to access a combination of services e.g. TV, Phone, Internet and Computer at each socket.
- High quality Wall Sockets ensure an excellent connection to your TV's, Speakers, Internet etc.
- Available in a Variety of Finishes including white, brass and chrome

YOU GET ONE CHANCE TO WIRE YOUR HOME, ITS IMPORTANT YOU GET IT RIGHT.

smarthomes

GYLES QUAY, DUNDALK, COUNTY LOUTH, IRELAND
T   +353 042 937 6678
F   +353 042 937 6679
E   INFO@SMARTHOMES.IE

WWW.SMARTHOMES.IE

View along drive towards entrance

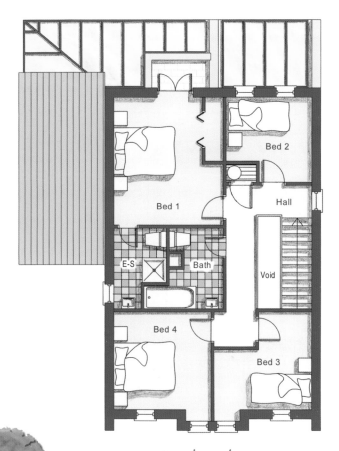

2023

First Floor Plan

A traditional two-storey chalet type development arranged off a central staircase. The family area and living room are located around the kitchen, which offers the flexibility to open both rooms onto the kitchen and the potential for an open plan house.

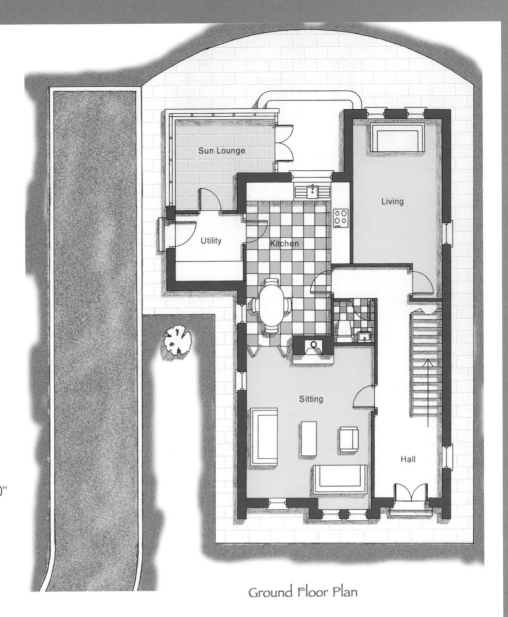

Ground Floor Plan

Four Bedrooms.
Kitchen/Dining - 11' 06''x16' 10''
Living - 9' 10''x15' 01''
Sitting - 14' 01''x16' 11''
Sun lounge - 11' 00''x9' 04''
Bed 1 -12' 00''x13' 05''
Bed 2 -9' 04''x8' 11''
Bed 3 - 10' 08''x11' 06''
Bed 4 - 10' 08''x11' 06''
Overall Length - 31' 05''
Overall Width - 42' 09''
Floor Area - 1669 sq. ft.

View from rear towards Sun Lounge

For **Construction Costs**
See Pages 74 & 75

55

Main view towards front porch

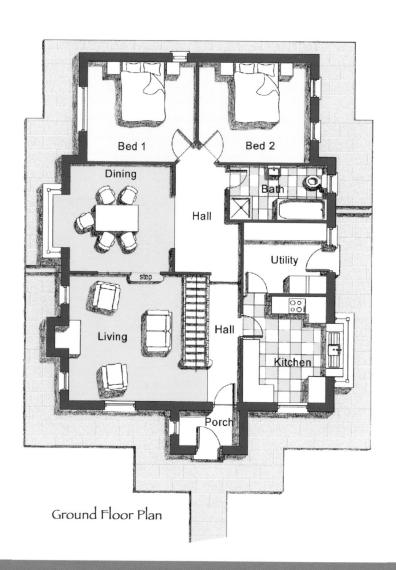

Ground Floor Plan

For **Construction Costs**
See Pages 74 & 75

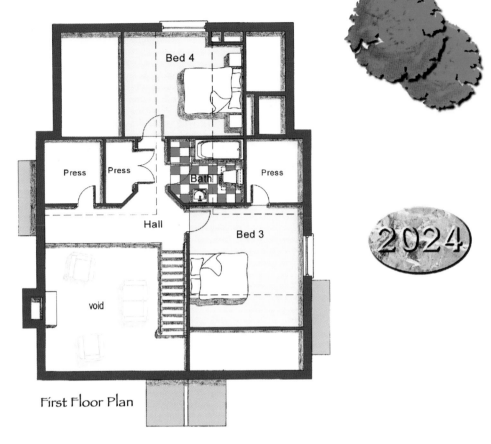

Bed 4

Press   Press   Press

Bath

Hall

Bed 3

void

2024

First Floor Plan

Four Bedrooms.
Kitchen - 9' 06"x11' 11"
Living - 19' 08"x14' 03"
Dining - 11' 10"x11' 10"
Bed 1 - 12' 06"x11' 02"
Bed 2 -12' 10"x11' 02"
Bed 3 - 13' 01"x13' 07"
Bed 4 - 13' 07"x11' 08"
Overall Length - 35' 10"
Overall Width - 44' 09"
Floor Area - 1757 sq. ft.

As with some of the previous illustrations, this house has a deeper emphasis, leaving it suited to a narrower site. The main feature of this design is the open plan staircase and vaulted ceiling over the living room, leaving the first floor landing acting as a balcony over the living space. Ideal for families who intend to spend most time in living/dining spaces.

Copyright 2000 Plan-A-Home

Front view towards main entrance

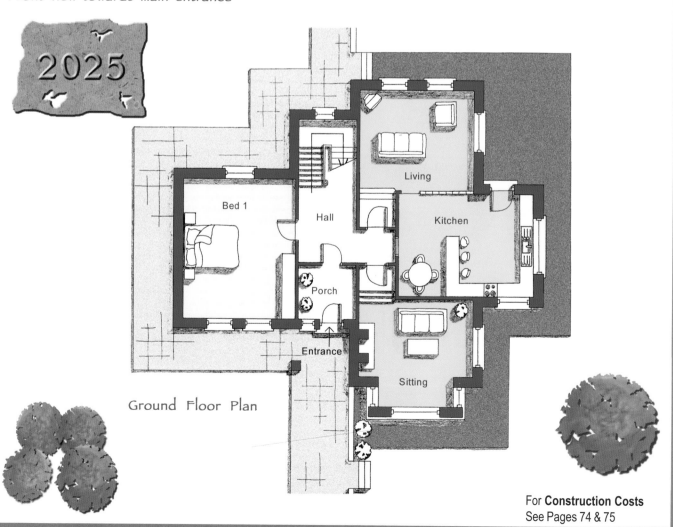

2025

Bed 1

Hall

Living

Kitchen

Porch

Entrance

Sitting

Ground Floor Plan

For **Construction Costs**
See Pages 74 & 75

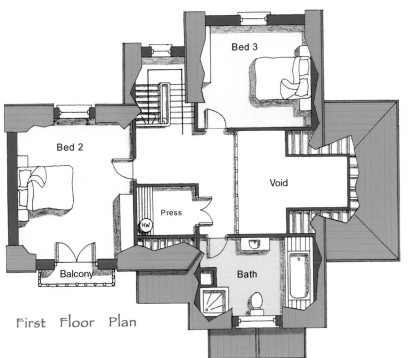

Bed 3

Bed 2

Void

Press

HW

Balcony

Bath

First Floor Plan

View from front right

The compact arrangement of this house allows the family the opportunity to have a visual link between the main habitable areas. The form of the house offers a charming small-scale space and belies the amount of accommodation within. This design could be greatly increased in floor area yet still hold the same character.

View from rear towards living room and kitchen projection

Three Bedrooms.
Kitchen - 21' 03"x14' 90"
Living - 13' 00"x14' 09"
Sitting - 14' 06"x14' 09"
Bed 1 - 11' 06"x14' 09"
Bed 2 - 19' 06"x13' 03"
Bed 3 - 16' 06"x13' 00"
Overall Length - 45' 03"
Overall Width - 45' 03"
Floor Area - 1866 sq. ft.

View Towards Sun Lounge

Copyright 2000 Plan-A-Home

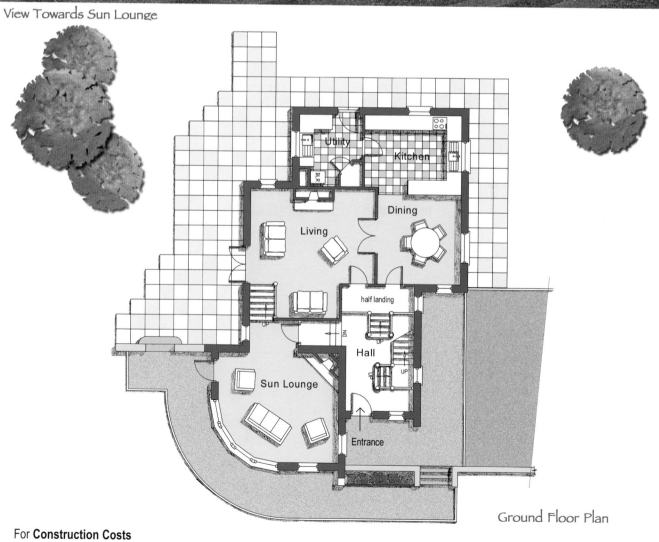

Utility

Kitchen

BLR

Dining

Living

half landing

UP

DN

Hall

UP

Sun Lounge

Entrance

Ground Floor Plan

For **Construction Costs**
See Pages 74 & 75

A luxury three bedroom home, designed for a sloping site with north-south axis. The sun lounge designed to have a southerly aspect to benefit from the full natural light throughout the day. The master bedroom opens onto a concealed terrace, which is made private by the extending parapet wall. Lots of steps and ballustrading give the ground floor a distinctive appearance.

View towards main entrance

View towards rear of house with patio doors leading to living room

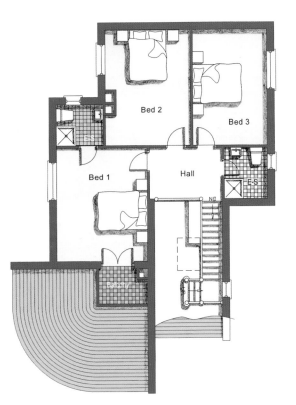

First Floor Plan

2026

Three Bedrooms.
Kitchen - 13' 01"x10' 06"
Dining - 11' 04"x11' 10"
Living - 16' 11"x16' 11"
Sun Lounge - 16' 05"x14' 05"
Bed 1 - 14' 10"x12' 02"
Bed 2 -11' 05"x15' 02"
Bed 3 -10' 02"x15' 02"
Overall Length - 34' 08"
Overall Width - 49' 10"
Floor Area - 1743 sq. ft.

BEDROOMS

All bedrooms should be different to reflect the differing needs and aspirations of the individual user. There is no limit to what uses a bedroom may have or indeed as to where the bedroom may be located.

In some instances the bedroom is located at the top of the house to optimise the availability of daylight, and in others it may be at ground level to optimise the access to the garden and external areas. In your consideration of a suitable location for the bedroom many factors come into play including the need to be near the bathroom, children's bedroom or readily accessible to the balcony.

The design of the bedroom offers you an opportunity to create a semi-private space where you can indulge your imagination and satisfy your physical needs for quiet undisturbed sleep while at the same time providing a haven for personal contemplative reflection.

The primary function of a bedroom is for sleeping, waking and starting the day. The dominant feature of the room should therefore be the bed. By establishing the type of bed, whether it be existing or new, you will form a clear picture of the layout, mood and size of the bedroom at an early stage of the house design development. Further consideration for the room may include whether it would be required to double as a work space, study or gym etc. By developing an early understanding of the physical functional and spatial requirements of the house such questions as regards bedroom sizes and locations can be quickly incorporated in the context of overall house design.

Lighting within bedrooms is primarily provided by either natural early morning light or artificial light by night. Ideally the bedroom should be orientated to the Irish climate, to the East and South-East corner of the site, to maximize the availability of natural light within the room. Bedrooms are occupied primarily at night and as such artificial light will be used for a significant period of the time.

Artificial light in bedrooms is required in a similar fashion as the lighting in kitchens and offices, it being necessary to cater for a variety of different functions ranging from general background light, task lights for dressing and applying make-up, reading lights located at the bed-head, to spot lights for highlighting important decorative features or items of furniture.

The decoration and design of the bedroom play a very important role in developing the mood of the room. Colours such as pure white may be used to enhance limited natural sunlight in wintertime or to reflect artificial light while darker brown or green could be used to mute the light and thus create a more intimate mood.

The ceiling finish in the bedroom, unlike many other rooms, should be given more consideration than is usually the case as the main vantage point for viewing the bedroom is from the horizontal position. This also reminds us that there may be elements of the room that may need to be arranged so as to be viewed from the bed - for example window cill heights may be dropped or roof-lights located above the bed-head and other items of furniture arranged to be easily accessible from the bed.

Floors to bedrooms should be smooth and soft. Even where a hard surface such as timber or tiles is proposed it would be prudent to soften these surfaces with large rugs and mats. It should be noted that carpets within bedrooms are not subject to the same degree of wear as those in hall or living room areas and therefore the most expensive quality of carpet is not a necessity.

Furniture in bedrooms is crucially important as bedrooms often tend to untidiness and therefore provision of adequate storage is important. Storage space may be provided by built-in cupboards or ready-made wardrobes. Storage should be allowed for a number of objects of different sizes from shoes to coats.
Built-in dressing room and en-suites may be included if space allows. There are no set dimensions for these spaces as sizes can range from that of a small wardrobe to an average size room and larger.

Children's bedrooms will change radically as the children grow. A child's bedroom may start out as toddler's nursery and develop into a private teenage den used for "hanging out", listening to music and entertaining friends. The bedroom, irrespective of a child's age, should offer a stimulating safe environment in which a quite considerable period of a child's home life might be spent.

Children's rooms will be required to suit a number of functions ranging from sleeping to studying and playing.
Particular attention should be paid to storage in children's bedrooms. This could allow exciting spaces to be created when combined with other functions of the room.

BATHROOMS

The average sized bathroom in Ireland today is just 6ft x 9ft. This, of course, includes all existing stock, with the smaller bathrooms being found in the speculative semi-detached market. There are many important factors to be taken into account when attempting to get the bathroom right. For a room which has, traditionally, been designed as the smallest room in the house, its duties, functions and responsibilities can be a heavy weight on its often meagre shoulders.

Of all the aspects to a bathroom which must be considered the two which stand out as being most crucial are location and comfort.

The bathroom must be located so that it is readily accessible to all the people who wish to use it. This will vary considerably depending on the number of bathrooms which are to be constructed within the dwelling. In modern dwellings it would be very unusual to have just one bathroom. It would now be considered normal that at least the master bedroom would have its own private bathroom or en-suite. In a large dwelling of five bedrooms or more a second en-suite should be considered, allowing the three remaining rooms to share the main bathroom.

Another aspect which must be considered is whether or not the main bathroom will be utilised for general daily use or if a separate w.c. is available. Often a w.c. will be located to the rear of a dwelling - accessed from a utility room. This can be particularly useful for children playing outside - avoiding the need for pulling buckets of sand, mud and other undesirables through the house in times of emergency. In a two-story dwelling a dilemma often arises. One wants to be able to facilitate visitors by having a w.c. on the ground floor. However, if this w.c. is accessed from a utility or back hall for reasons described above, one may be reluctant to send visitors into this area. In this situation it is more prudent to consider the general needs of the family. Visitors are usually more than happy to use a first floor bathroom which is likely to be the bathroom into which most thought and expense has gone.

Finally don't think of the bathroom as simply a place to take care of hygiene needs. Enjoy the room and the atmosphere which can be created therein.

courtesy: Shires Bathrooms

courtesy: Shires Bathrooms

The second item we must consider in the bathroom is comfort. This will mean different things to different people and take in items such as layout, heating and decor.

When designing a bathroom - particularly on the first floor - thought must be given to the position and direction of services. Appliances should, ideally, be positioned so that drainage can now run in the same direction as floor joists. Where this is not feasible raised areas within the bathroom can be considered. These can be an attractive feature while at the same time hiding pipework.

Because the bathroom can be an expensive room to fit out, it is important to get the layout right. This is doubly the case when one considers that once appliances are fixed, they cannot be readily relocated.

Traditionally baths were located on one wall with the w.c., wash hand basin and possibly bidet on another. Bathroom layout is now moving on and where space allows it is not uncommon to position the bath in the centre of the room. Here an antique or reproduction bath can form the main focus possibly on a raised platform within the room. Alternatively, and if the house design allows, the bath can be sunk into the floor. Should the height not be available in the floor below, a similar effect can be created by providing steps up to a raised area into which the bath is recessed.

It must be considered whether or not a separate shower is required within a bathroom. If space allows, this will afford greater comfort for those who prefer the convenience of a shower to a bath. The numerous fittings available including body sprays, double showers and even steam units. If space is not abundant, a shower can be fitted above the bath with either a curtain or screen surround. Again the variety of fitting available including screens and curtains for corner baths allows for maximum choice.

The type of suite chosen should, in some way, reflect the style of room one wishes to create. The bathroom is a place where, if budget permits, we can allow our imagination a free rein. With anything from great gothic indulgence to lavish Romanesque with marble floors, baths and porticos or traditional free standing claw foot roll-top bath and washed timber paneling.

Whichever style is chosen, think seriously before purchasing a suite in a strong color. It is very hard to improve on classic white which is practically guaranteed to stay in fashion.

Finishes which can be applied within a bathroom are various and the materials used are only limited by budget. Tiling has been and continues to be the most popular finish. One possible drawback with this is the costs involved if one wants a change of decor. For this reason, it may be worth considering tiling to dado height and applying a paint or paper finish above this.

courtesy: Shires Bathrooms

The bathroom should be well-heated. Gone are the days when bathrooms were merely used for a brisk wash at either end of the day. People are now spending more time in the bathroom and, with options such as large Jacuzzi baths, fireplaces, televisions and exercise equipment, the bathroom can be a place to unwind after a tough day, to get away from the kids or plan a romantic meeting with a little bubbly - be it Dom Perignon or Mr. Bubbles.

Heating is usually provided either by radiant or under-floor heating. On a ground floor under-floor heating is by far the most desirable. It provides an even, comfortable heat and a warm surface on which to walk. Under-floor heating can also be utilised on the first floor but it can sometimes be difficult to achieve. If radiators are used ensure they are located in positions where they will not cause burns when accidentally brushed against. Towel rail radiators can be an attractive alternative to the standard radiator. They come in a variety of styles and have obvious practical advantages.

View from front garden towards porch entrance

2027

This deceptively large three bedroom, one and a half storey, dwelling captures the spirit of a gate lodge whilst the open plan arrangement of the reception rooms results in an exceptionally spacious interior. this is then complimented by the generous upper floor landing.

View along driveway towards front entrance

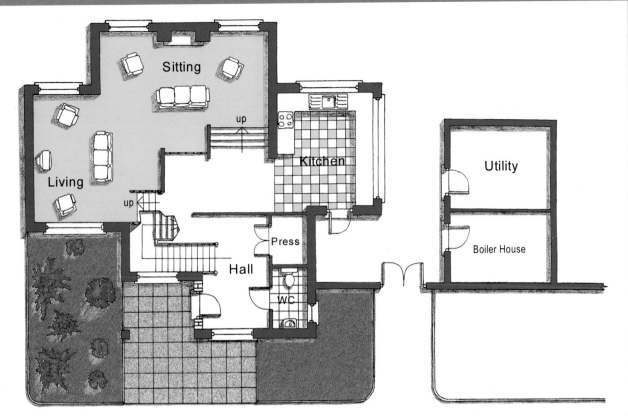

Ground Floor Plan

Three Bedrooms.
Kitchen - 10' 10"x12' 02"
Living - 10' 10"x14' 01"
Sitting - 19' 00"x12' 06"
Bed 1 -13' 02"x13' 02"
Bed 2 -13' 09"x9' 10"
Bed 3 - 14' 05"x11' 02"
Overall Length - 40' 08"
Overall Width - 34' 01"
Floor Area - 1554 sq. ft.

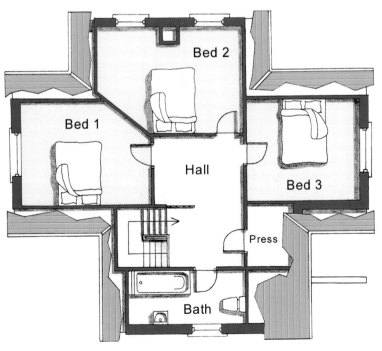

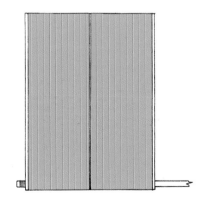

First Floor Plan

For **Construction Costs**
See Pages 74 & 75

View towards front of house

2028

Three Bedrooms.
Kitchen - 9' 04''x11' 02''
Living/Dining - 16' 05''x20' 04'
Bed 1 -10' 10''x13' 07''
Bed 2 -11' 07''x10' 08''
Bed 3 - 12' 00''x12' 06''
Overall Length - 34' 05''
Overall Width - 34' 09''
Floor Area - 1458 sq. ft.

For **Construction Costs**
See Pages 74 & 75

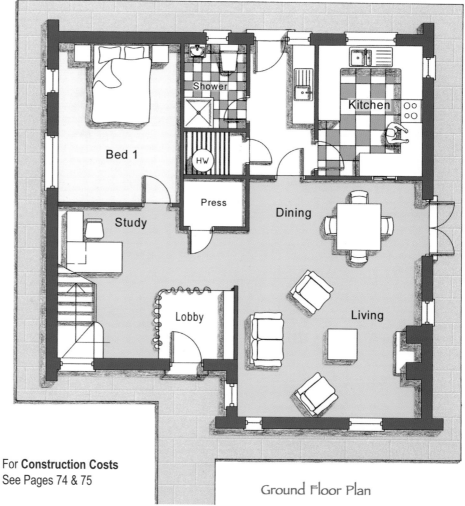

Ground Floor Plan

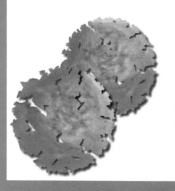

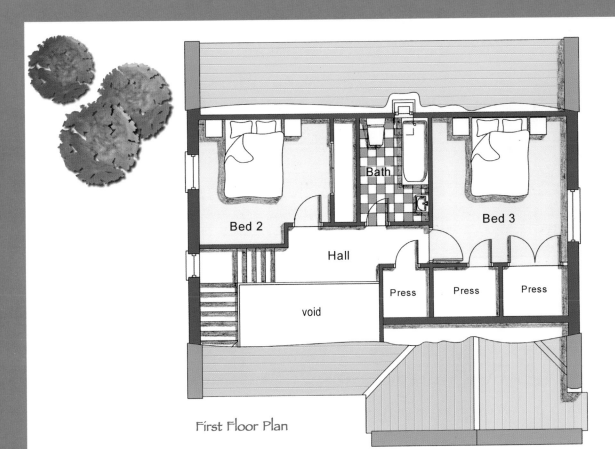

Bed 2

Bath

Bed 3

Hall

void

Press

Press

Press

First Floor Plan

This design draws heavily from the rural vernacular of the traditional cottage but, on closer examination, features many modern touches; from the open plan living space to the first floor gallery, which overlooks the study area.
A spiral staircase could replace the traditional stair illustrated here and become a visual feature to the room.

View from front right

View from front garden towards porch entrance

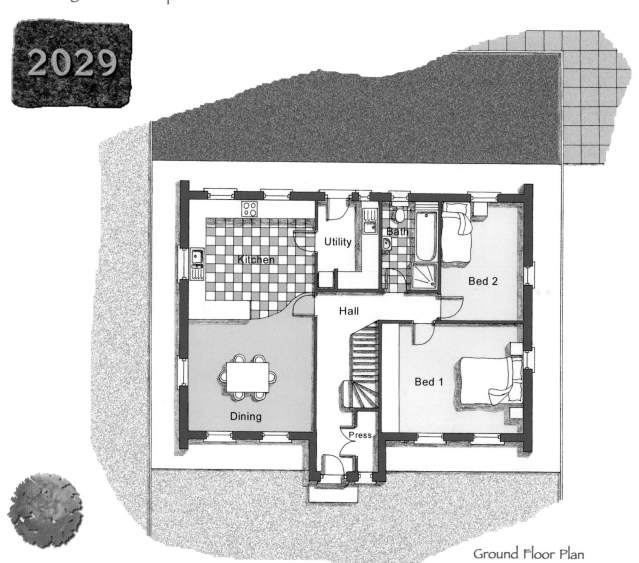

2029

Kitchen

Utility

Bath

Bed 2

Hall

Dining

Bed 1

Press

Ground Floor Plan

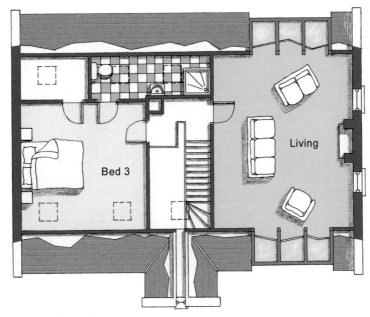

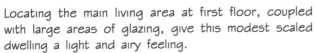

Bed 3

Living

First Floor Plan

Locating the main living area at first floor, coupled with large areas of glazing, give this modest scaled dwelling a light and airy feeling.

The great advantage of a fisrt floor living space is that it exploits the potential view to a maximum.

This traditional vernacular dwelling offers a contemporary alternative behind the facade.

Three Bedrooms.
Kitchen/Dining - 14' 01"x24' 07"
Living - 15' 09"x24' 07"
Bed 1 -15' 09"x11' 10"
Bed 2 -9' 02"x12' 06"
Bed 3 - 14' 01"x13' 03"
Overall Length - 39' 04"
Overall Width - 31' 08"
Floor Area - 1755 sq. ft.

View towards rear

For Construction Costs
See Pages 74 & 75

View from front garden towards porch entrance

Four Bedrooms.
Kitchen/Dining - 19' 00"x17' 05"
Living - 15' 01"x12' 10"
Study - 19' 10"x8' 10"
Bed 1 -15' 01"x12' 10"
Bed 2 -15' 01"x11' 06"
Bed 3 - 9' 11"x15' 01"
Overall Length - 37' 05"
Overall Width - 38' 09"
Floor Area - 1756 sq. ft.

Ground Floor Plan

Bed 2

Bed 3

Bath

En-Suite

Bed 1

A compact three bedroom house of great character.

Notable for it's long kitchen\dining room, generous reception hall, en-suite master bedroom and downstairs study. The study could, of course, become a fourth bedroom if prefered.

First Floor Plan

View along driveway towards front entrance

For **Construction Costs**
See Pages 74 & 75

73

Construction Costs

As building costs vary greatly throughout the country our intention is to indicate prices typical for general areas. If you are on the border of the highlighted regions your price will fall somewhere between those given. To help identify projected overall expenditure we have broken the prices into three stages.

Stage A ~ Main Structure

This includes for all works (material and labour) in Constructing your house: foundations, walls, roof, plastering, plumbing, electrical and joinery.
See Guideline Specifications on Page 75 for details. Stone or brick finishes are shown on some houses for illustration purposes only. These finishes are **NOT** included in the guideline cost.
For brick cladding add approximately 10% to the Stage A amount.
For stone cladding add approximately 20% to the Stage A amount.

All costings are based on traditional construction methods (using cavity blockwork walls) and a contract procurement method - employing a contractor through selective tendering rather than utilising direct labour.
Guideline prices will also be reasonably accurate for timber frame construction as cost differences are negligible compared to traditional build.

Stage B ~ Fit Out

This section has deliberately been kept separate as you will probably want to control your own budget on these.
Items include:
Kitchen units
Utility units
Sanitaryware -   as shown
Fireplaces-   as shown
Painting and decorating
Wall tiling – assume to ceiling height
Floor finishes – assume 25% of floor area covered
                              with ceramics and/or hardwood
Stairs-   Hardwood, where applicable
Patent roof glazing- Where applicable

Ranges, stoves and wardrobes, although shown, are not included.

The amount shown in Stage B includes Stages 'A' amounts.

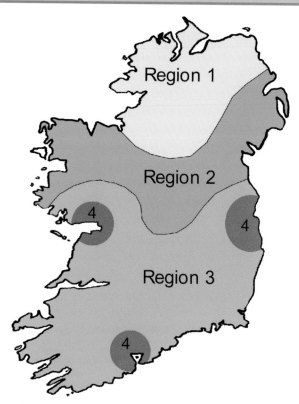

NOTE: Region 4 (areas in red) - It is currently impossible to accurately predict pricing trends in these areas. However, developments in region 4 may increase by up to 10% to 20 % of region 3.
Other cities may also experience similar trends of escalating construction costs.

Stage C ~ Site Works

This is a provisional amount for all site works and services based on a green field site of approximately half an acre and is assumed to include for:
footpaths, tarmac driveways, sewerage, storm water and water supply.
Fencing or boundary walls have not been included in this amount.
A serviced site will be less expensive to develop.
The amounts shown in Stage C includes Stage 'B'.

SITE PURCHASE PRICE NOT INCLUDED

plan	stage	region 1	region 2	region 3
KEY				
2001	A	83,915	93,565	104,055
	B	102,617	114,419	127,247
	C	113,184	126,200	140,348

To read costings:
1. Refer to plan number - for example 2001.
2. Find your region - e.g. Roscommon is Region 2.
3. The Chart indicates expenditure at Stages outlined i.e. Shell complete equals stage A = €93,565 but to complete house to a moving in stage = €126,200

Stage A

Roof :-   Concrete roof tiles
External walls: Cavity, smooth rendered
Facia/soffit: uPVC or Aluminium.
Windows: uPVC, double glazed
External doors: uPVC, double glazed
Internal doors: White pressed 6 panel
                     doors
Skirting/Arch.:   Softwood or M.D.F.
Heating/plumb.:   Conventional system with
                     rads and cylinder
Electrical: Reasonable standard of
                     electrics.

Stage B

See previous page

Stage C

See previous page

Please Note:
The prices listed here are for guideline purposes only and are indicative of contract values current in €uro's at Summer 2006.

design	stage	region 1	region 2	region 3
2001	A	83,915	93,565	104,055
	B	102,617	114,419	127,247
	C	113,184	126,200	140,348
2002	A	123,161	137,324	152,719
	B	146,188	163,000	181,274
	C	160,061	178,468	198,476
2003	A	94,684	105,573	117,408
	B	114,353	127,504	141,798
	C	125,464	139,893	155,576
2004	A	98,847	110,215	122,572
	B	121,156	135,088	150,232
	C	134,684	150,172	167,008
2005	A	108,804	121,316	134,917
	B	134,530	150,001	166,817
	C	147,673	164,655	183,113
2006	A	135,139	150,680	167,572
	B	164,947	183,916	204,534
	C	177,498	197,910	220,098
2007	A	120,915	134,820	149,935
	B	147,273	164,208	182,618
	C	160,659	179,134	199,217
2008	A	89,980	100,327	111,574
	B	113,091	126,096	140,234
	C	125,093	139,479	155,116
2009	A	96,354	107,436	119,480
	B	120,642	134,516	149,596
	C	133,254	148,578	165,235
2010	A	118,509	132,138	146,951
	B	144,566	161,191	179,262
	C	157,635	175,763	195,467
2011	A	103,487	115,388	128,324
	B	126,841	141,428	157,283
	C	139,397	155,429	172,854
2012	A	88,976	99,207	110,329
	B	108,395	120,861	134,410
	C	119,880	133,667	148,651
2013	A	120,809	134,702	149,802
	B	139,488	155,529	172,965
	C	151,254	168,648	187,554

design	stage	region 1	region 2	region 3
2014	A	101,636	113,388	126,028
	B	122,026	136,060	151,313
	C	134,311	149,756	166,544
2015	A	82,742	92,258	102,600
	B	98,001	109,272	121,521
	C	109,137	121,689	135,331
2016	A	121,218	135,159	150,311
	B	144,579	161,205	179,278
	C	158,651	176,896	196,727
2017	A	104,039	116,003	129,008
	B	123,566	137,776	153,222
	C	137,818	153,667	170,894
2018	A	108,247	120,696	134,227
	B	128,850	143,667	159,773
	C	141,260	157,505	175,163
2019	A	113,395	126,435	140,610
	B	134,000	149,410	166,161
	C	149,039	166,179	184,809
2020	A	110,885	123,637	137,497
	B	131,959	147,135	163,630
	C	144,875	161,535	179,644
2021	A	144,588	161,216	179,290
	B	169,064	188,507	209,639
	C	187,518	209,082	232,523
2022	A	99,349	110,774	123,193
	B	118,398	132,014	146,815
	C	130,073	145,030	161,290
2023	A	128,767	143,576	159,672
	B	170,347	189,936	211,229
	C	186,772	208,250	231,597
2024	A	118,703	132,353	147,191
	B	141,462	157,730	175,413
	C	155,411	173,282	192,709
2025	A	114,555	127,729	142,049
	B	133,968	149,374	166,121
	C	145,387	162,107	180,280
2026	A	142,611	159,011	176,836
	B	170,304	189,888	211,176
	C	189,292	211,061	234,723
2027	A	115,633	128,932	143,386
	B	137,671	153,504	170,713
	C	153,755	171,438	126,157
2028	A	110,794	123,535	137,384
	B	131,443	146,559	162,990
	C	144,098	160,670	178,682
2029	A	137,505	153,319	170,507
	B	162,362	181,033	201,329
	C	177,594	198,017	220,217
2030	A	129,389	144,269	160,443
	B	154,259	172,000	191,282
	C	169,501	188,994	210,181

Environmentally Responsive and Energy Conscious Design

The nature of domestic design in this country has seen considerable change in recent years. As people demand more from their living enviroments they seek a more site specific and enviromentally sensitive approach to the design of the houses in which they live.

In the following section HMG and CMG Associates, Architects, explore the principal issues likely to be of concern in addressing these ever changing and increasingly important aspects of house design. Outlined below are some strategic considerations to inform design in the future.

External Enviroment

- Site Selection, Natural Features, Topography
- Sun Path & Orientation
- Location of House on Site
- Use of Natural Shelter
- Planting & Landscape

Internal living Enviroment

- Relationship of Internal to External Spaces
- Glazed Elements (passive solar design)
- Building Materials
- Heat Conservation/Insulation
- Healthy Living Enviroments
- Sustainability (Energy Choices)
- Smart Design & Intelligent Buildings

Energy Solutions for the Environmentally Responsible Home

- Conventional Energy Solutions
- Non Conventional Energy Systems (Including Renewable Energy)
- Domestic Energy Usage - The Way Forward

"The planet is not ours to own - we are merely custodians of our childrens' future"

Environmentally Responsive and Energy Conscious Design

Site Orientation

In the consideration of the potential energy performance of any development a series of strategic decisions are taken, each having a direct affect on that which follows. The first decision is made at the point at which you select a site and the location of any development on that site.

The key areas of consideration are:

Site Selection

Prevailing winds: The location of the house on the site should be considered with the criteria of making the best uses of any natural protection the site offers. Balanced against this are the ground conditions at the house location, along with environmental, visual and ecological attributes of the site such as flood plains, rock outcrops which should be fully established and understood before the final selection of a site is made.

House Location

A key consideration of where to locate a house on site is the impact the development will have on the surrounding landscape. This consideration is a major concern to the planning department, An Taisce, the Department of the Environment and historical organisations. The preservation of historical monuments and the protection of important geological and topographical features must be considered.

At an early planning stage the protection offered by natural shelterbelts, mounding and other existing features should be established. The diagrams on page 78 indicate a schematic arrangement of how certain aspects of site protection can be offered. It should be remembered that the existing planting and topography of a house offers the opportunity for both shelter from cold winds in a temperate/cold climate and shading from solar heat gain in a warm climate.

A suitably knowledgeable architect will be in a position to offer useful consultation on the selection of a site and house location strategy.

Orientation of House

The energy efficiency of a house is determined by its ability to have natural sources of energy to compliment and meet the energy needs and conversely it's ability to retain and recycle the energy/heat that has been inputted into it. The most significant source of energy is the sun.

In the orientation of a house the relationship of the house to the sun's path is critical. The house should be arranged to maximise the surface area exposed to the sun. It should be remembered that the angle of the sun alters from season to season. In Ireland's temperate climate the demand for complimentary sources of heat is greatest in the winter. Walls should be angled to suit the angle of the sun in mid-winter and orientated South. The form of the house should not only address the best aspect of the sun's path but additionally should allow surfaces for the inclusion of such features as solar panels, evacuated tubes and other energy saving/producing devices. In addition to the orientation of the house the house form could address the issue of the building's wind resistance and hence its heat loss.

Shelter Belts

The effect of wind on the thermal performance of a house can be judged by simply blowing on the back of your hand. This effect would be even more noticeable by wetting the back of your hand and repeating the exercise. The same cooling effect is produced by wind blowing on a wet façade. Therefore, the importance of screening buildings from prevailing wind where possible and keeping horizontal surfaces dry must be appreciated. Where this is not possible or there is not an existing, established shelterbelt, introduced landscaping can be used to provide screening and compliment the amenity of the house. Where possible the planting of indigenous trees and shrubs should be used as their suitability for the environment is tested and proven. The soil conditions of the site, such as site soakage will reduce the amount of energy expense and difficulty in exploiting the land.

The best placed person to advise and select a suitable system from the baffling combinations of variables which contribute to an energy efficient approach is a suitably qualified consultant.

Environmentally Responsive and Energy Conscious Design

In the initial consideration of a site and the selection of a location for the house one should

Consider:
Use of natural features
Use of hard and soft landscaping
Use of indigenous broadleaf variety of trees
Local mounding of landscape to mitigate visual impact
Availability of services
Environmental impact

Use natural and artificial features to shelter dwelling from prevailing winds while allowing maximum solar benefit.

Consider:
Orientation
Shelter belts
Day light/ sun path
Prevailing winds
Views
Ground conditions

Hazardous materials on site
Natural energy potential
Privacy
Future extendability

Site house in landscape to maximize natural shelter, sun path and general aspect

---

INTERNAL LIVING ENVIRONMENTS

Sun Path & Orientation
Just as a building's location in its natural landscape should be considered in a sensitive and thoughtful manner, the inter-relationship of spaces within the internal living environment of a dwelling should be given equal consideration.

Chief among matters for consideration at this point should be the house's orientation. South facing areas should be used throughout the day as family room and living room accommodation, whereas ideally the kitchen and kitchen/dining area might be located below a master bedroom in the eastern part of the house, thus taking advantage of early morning sun. In a similar fashion, consideration should be given to the location of living room/drawing room areas on the western side of dwellings, taking advantage of the evening sun with patio or terraced areas opening from this room. Planning of the internal spaces of a house in this manner creates a certain rhythm and logic to a house's internal spatial organisation, and maximises the considerable benefits to be gained by intelligent use of natural light.

Passive Solar Design
The sun's energy can also be used to great effect when considering its heating potential in the design of integrated conservatory space in homes.

These spaces, often referred to, as "passive solar conservatories" are best located on the southerly aspect of a house where the greatest benefit can be gained from the sun's path (See figs. above). In this regard, conservatories traditionally seen as "bolt on" addition to existing houses can be more closely and seamlessly integrated into the house's design. This may also facilitate the conservatory's space being more centrally accessible from commonly used rooms at the heart of the home.

Transition Spaces
In recent years increasing attention is being paid by homebuilders to the provision of external spaces adjacent to commonly used areas of the house. These areas, often referred to as terraces, patios or decks, provide practical and increasingly useful additional space and act as a transition between internal and external space. Once again such elements should make best use of the sun's path and natural shelter in their orientation. Trees, ideally broad leafed and native in variety, can be planted in such a manner as to enclose external spaces, creating a comfortable and naturally sheltered external environment, and can also be continued into internal conservatory spaces, oxygenating air and filtering light. This planting also serves to better integrate a house with its natural landscape and to soften the harsh lines often evident in buildings located on open and exposed sites.

Environmentally Responsive and Energy Conscious Design

By taking this approach, we lessen the (potential) negative environmental impact likely to be caused by the location of dwellings in open areas. Softening the visual environmental impact the building is likely to have in an open natural environment can also have quantifiable environmental benefits.

Chief among these is the careful selection of building materials.

Selection of Building Materials

The sensitive use of locally found and naturally occurring building materials, such as wood and stone, can give rise to a much more energy efficient end product. Quantities of building materials conveyed large distances require the use of considerable amounts of energy in their transportation; just as materials which have complex and energy intensive production processes, such as aluminium and copper, require considerable amounts of energy in their fabrication.

It is of course unfair to be prescriptive where building materials are concerned, as their relative merits and de-merits might not always be so obvious; however, it is worthwhile pointing out that issues such as *sustainability*, *recyclability* and *local availability* should always be considered.

Heating, Lighting & Energy Conservation

Having considered the above matters, it is important to turn one's attention to conservation of energy used in heating and lighting the home, together with the creation of a healthy and pleasant living environment.

Considerable advances have been made in the development of more thermally efficient heating systems available for domestic design, for example:- thermal store cylinders which can be driven by various heating sources are now available, offering extremely high efficiency hot water storage.

Having arrived at an effective solution for the heating of a home, it is imperative that this heat is retained in an efficient manner. It is always advisable that dwellings should be thoroughly sealed and well insulated, and, in recent years, more and more people are opting to exceed current required insulation guidelines for traditional construction for housing.

A natural bi-product of a well sealed and thoroughly insulated home is the need for adequate ventilation both through the structure of the house for the protection of its fabric, and through the house's internal spaces for the creation of a healthy living environment.

Natural Ventilation

Adequate ventilation can be achieved in the traditional manner by openable windows or by trickle ventilation and permanent ventilation designed into window frames. In addition to the above in recent years increased interest has been shown by many in the use of natural ventilation systems. These systems often constituting simple ducts located on external wall or roof areas can now be combined with heat exchange systems allowing fresh air to be heated by warm exhaust air from kitchen and bathroom areas. Such natural air conditioning can be combined with air filtration systems to also provide clean environments for people with allergies to airborne particular matter.

Future Systems & Smart Design

In considering such current advances in building technology, it is often useful to look around the corner, so to speak, and consider what the future has to offer. To this end, the "future proofing" of internal living environments is an increasingly popular consideration. Although an ambitious sounding objective, "future proofing" of homes simply seeks to employ intelligent design so that extensive work is not required at a later stage to install new technology not envisaged at the time of construction, such as digital cabling, and ducting systems which will, in the future, be commonplace in many homes. Technical trunking can be installed in floor slabs or behind skirtings in order to easily accommodate possible future requirement. Irrelevant as it might seem to many at this point, it is a commonly held view of house designers that the future will see us demanding much more from the environments in which we live.

It is, for example, anticipated that houses will have at their core an electronic brain which will control everything from environmental monitoring systems and lighting, to Internet applications and the arming of security systems, etc. Although it may not be considered by many to be a practical requirement at this stage to accommodate such grandiose ambitions in the design of their home, it is often worthwhile to simply consider provision of basic facilities to allow future expansion if required. This can be done at the time of house construction for a fraction of what it will cost later.

The above are but a small number of design considerations from the external and organic to the internal and high-tech. These matters are best addressed by discussing them further with your architect.

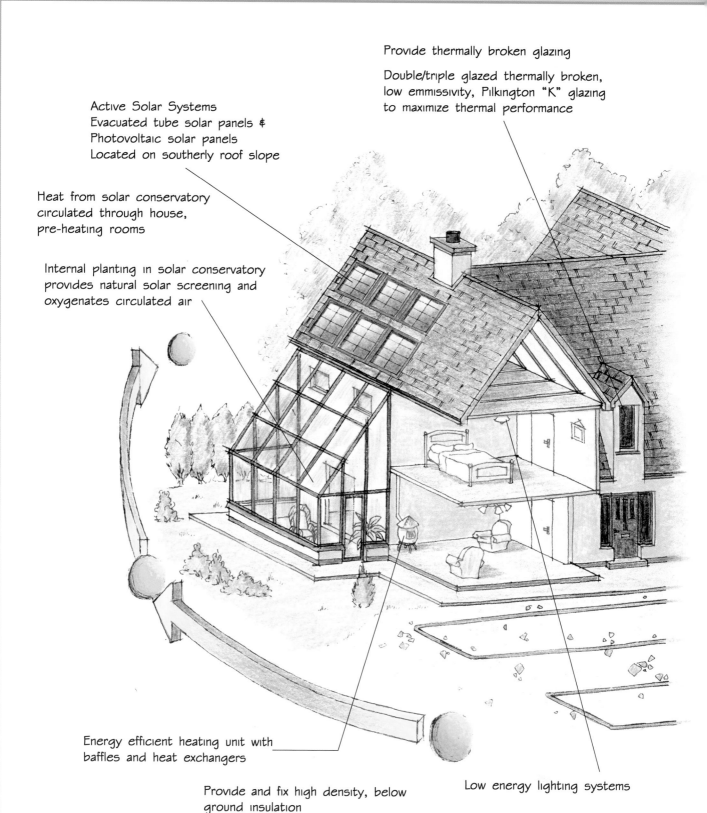

Provide thermally broken glazing

Double/triple glazed thermally broken, low emmissivity, Pilkington "K" glazing to maximize thermal performance

Active Solar Systems
Evacuated tube solar panels &
Photovoltaic solar panels
Located on southerly roof slope

Heat from solar conservatory circulated through house, pre-heating rooms

Internal planting in solar conservatory provides natural solar screening and oxygenates circulated air

Energy efficient heating unit with baffles and heat exchangers

Provide and fix high density, below ground insulation

Low energy lighting systems

Passive Solar Design
Solar conservatory located on southern elevation to maximise passive solar gain. Surface area of glazing to be maximised on this elevation

Additional Insulation
Aim to exceed prevailing guidelines by Super insulating building envelope

Energy Conscious Design

Recommended Improvements To Existing Thermal Performance

Installation of draft lobbies
Retrofitting of insulation systems
Replacement of existing glazing systems with double or triple glazing
Installation of integrated passive solar conservatory

Intelligent building systems

Energy management systems
Automated energy efficient control
of electrical and heating systems

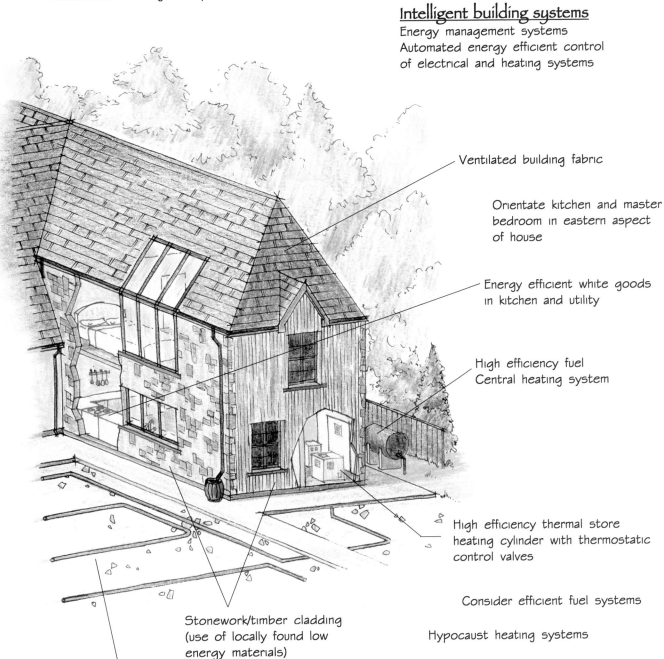

Ventilated building fabric

Orientate kitchen and master
bedroom in eastern aspect
of house

Energy efficient white goods
in kitchen and utility

High efficiency fuel
Central heating system

High efficiency thermal store
heating cylinder with thermostatic
control valves

Consider efficient fuel systems

Hypocaust heating systems

Radiant wall heating systems

Stonework/timber cladding
(use of locally found low
energy materials)

Ground source heat pump system

Efficiently zoned UF heating system
controlled by energy management system

Primary Heating Sources

Solid fuels oil, gas & electricity
Primary fuel sources can be complimented
by secondary forms such as wind energy,
ground source, passive and active solar.

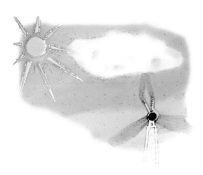

Energy Solutions for the Environmentally Responsible Home.

It takes 29,000kWhrs of energy to run the average three-bedroomed house for a year in Ireland, if all of this energy was supplied using day rate electricity it would cost approximately £1,750. Thankfully, very few households rely soley on electricity for their energy needs, but even with space heating energy being supplied by more conventional sources such as oil or coal an annual energy bill in excess of £1,200 is not unusual for most. A domestic household's annual energy consumption can be broken down into 74% for space heating, 12% for domestic hot water, 10% for electrical devices and 4% for cooking, it is apparent that focusing on the systems used for space heating and domestic hot water will have far reaching financial implications over the life cycle of a building The environmental implications of the way we heat our houses is also becoming an increasingly important issue, and, when you consider that the average oil burner emits over 7 metric tonnes of Carbon Dioxide into the atmosphere during the yearly heating/hot water cycle, the significance of domestic houses as a precursor to global warming are obvious.

Conventional Energy Solutions

All fossil fuel heating/hot water systems- those fuelled by coal, oil, LPG and natural gas-are energy intensive and environmentally damaging in their extraction, transportation and combustion. However, as they have been used for years they have well organised distribution networks to the consumer, in the case of oil and LPG lend themselves to automated systems, are highly responsive and due to their widespread usage are relatively inexpensive to use due to economies of scale, though their finite nature-15 years in the case of oil-is becoming increasingly responsible for dramatic bulk price increases.

In Ireland, unless you are fortunate enough to be in close proximity to a natural gas pipeline, being reliant on these fuels exposes you to the vagaries of international trade (this can be seen in the fact that domestic heating oil prices have risen 18% in the last year) and the risks of the global economy. If by reasons of availability or cost you are forced to use fossil fuels the enviromental impacts can be somewhat mitigated by the use of high efficiency boilers , careful matching of the boiler with your heating requirements and good control systems.

Wood is one of the most environmentally friendly fuels available to the domestic consumer; it is defined as 'Carbon Neutral' because only the amout of carbon dioxide absorbed during the growing cycle is released during combustion. It has the advantages of its ability to be produced locally thus reducing transportation costs, is in plentiful, renewable supply and genarally has good distribution networks. Wood is generally hand fed into free standing roomheaters with or without backboilers, however it is also available in pellet form as an automated process (this has the additional advantage of using byproducts from other wood conversion industries). Where the wood source is not a byproduct of another industry it is preferable that it should come from a 'Biomass' or other similar sustainable source.

Electricity is a popular heating energy source mainly for offices and flats where its comparatively low installation cost; convenience and non-requirement of on-site storage is a valuable asset. The downside is that it is expensive, however, the use of night rate storage type heaters can mitigate the cost but these are not very appropriate for most domestic users.

Although non-polluting at the point of use, electricity may use fossil fuel at the generator, however, it is now available from a number of companies generated by renewable energy allowing the domestic consumer to buy 'Green' at a price close to that of conventionally generated electricity.

Medium to large developments of houses may benefit from combining on site generation of electrical energy and heat generation (Combined Heat and Power or CHP). CHP can reduce the electrical distribution losses that are quite significant in conventional electriciy distribution and at the same time use the heat that is usually wasted during electrical production thus developing a high efficiency system. However, many of these systems are fossil fuel based so they should be used with caution.

Non Conventional Energy Systems (including Renewable Energy)

For the most part non-conventional energy systems will apply to more rural locations where large site, open aspect and lessor proximity to neighbours, distance to power lines is conducive to installing these systems, there are however examples of successful urban developments where they have been skillfully integrated into group schemes. The image of the independent energy house with windmill and solar panels, may seem the panacea for many, but in reality the economies of installing such systems will make them uneconomical for all but the most isolated of sites. Extracting energy from sun, wind or water sources is usually expensive, inevitably involves expensive storage as often the energy isn't available when it is required, requires a technical know how for the user and often must be taken in parallel with conventional systems such as a connection to the grid or solid fuel boiler backup. Such investment is beyond the realms of most householders and unless the government intervenes to provide incentives these systems are likely to remain so.

One technology that is available to the average house builder that generally uses renewable energy as its' source, and is a robust well proven technology is the Heat Pump; all matter contains energy, -even well below the freezing point of water-heat pumps capture this energy in much the same way that a refrigerator extracts heat from food in the fridge and vent it as heat on the cooling fins at the back of the fridge. In our climate seawater and the ground-whose energy originally came from the sun-have been proven to be the most sensible source of this energy, and, as the only power needed to extract this energy is that used in pumping a refrigerant around a collector, the cost of running these systems is highly competetive, indeed may be as little as one third of the cost of running a comparative oil based system! If the electricity used to power this system came from a 'Green' supplier it could be viewed as a sytem powered entirely by renewable energy.

In our climate solar panels- which generally transfer the sun's energy to water or air-make little sense as a source of domestic space heating energy, however as a means of

supplementing domestic hot water needs in the summer-saves putting on the immersion for hot water-they are ideal and there is evidence that a 4m² array can supply up to 60% of a households annual hot water requirements. The costs of implementing such systems vary widely, but the DIY enthusiast in conjunction with a kit supplied from some of the manufacturers could provide a solution that would pay for itself over 10 years.

Photovoltaics- which convert the suns energy to electricity rather than transfer to water or air-are not an ideal source of even supplement for domestic heating/hot water in Ireland for much the same reason as solar panels. They are much more expensive than solar panels for a similar power output and are ideally suited to remote applications requiring low power consumption such as navigation buoys, signal repeaters or weather stations.

A small windmill (2.5kw) which gives it's highest ouput during the winter months could help reduce space heating costs, but to make it economically feasible the ability to store it's output as heat (as opposed to electricity) in some type of thermal accumulator (generally a highly insulated water storage container in excess of 1 m³) is essential; but as stated previously the cost of most systems will be prohibitive for most.

Hydro, Geothermal and wave energy are some of the many other possible sources of renewable energy, but as with windmills their economies of installation become increasingly prohibitive unless used in group schemes. CHP, incineration, land fill gas, and gasification are other non-conventional technologies that are available as domestic energy sources; land fill gas in particular has been used in this country for housing developments. Many of these technologies have received negative press regarding their potential negative environmental effects and should be assessed with caution, however, the ability to properly dispose of waste and at the same provide a reliable energy supply should be assessed with a positive attitude.

Domestic Energy Usage - The Way Forward.

We have discussed some of the options available relating to the selection of heating/ hot water systems for domestic houses, this discussion is not intended to be a comprehensive analysis of the issues or technologies involved-the range of technologies is too vast- instead, it is intended as an aid to a person building or buying a house to achieve a picture of the wider issues associated with making such decisions. All too often the life cycle costs of conventional energy systems are overlooked in the shadow of system installation costs and this must be addressed by both designers and users alike.

There are many well proven energy efficient space/water heating systems available to suit all budgets ranging from high efficiency oil or gas boilers to integrated solar panel/wind turbine solutions. Systems based on renewable energy benefit from careful integration into the building structure-ideally during the design phase-however, items such as condensing burners can very often be simply interchanged with the existing burners. Whatever energy system you decide to install it is essential that it is viewed as an integrated unit with the building as a whole using passive design principles; increased insulation and comprehensive energy control systems. It is worth noting that Part L of the 1997 Building Regulations (Conservation of Fuel and Energy) comprehensively deals with the requirements of all buildings to achieve acceptable standards on energy performance.

Finally, the simplest way to reduce our domestic energy bill is to reduce our consumption; fluorescent bulbs; free standing solid fuel stoves as opposed to open fires; timer switches on appliances; use of night-rate electricity for washing and drying machines; is that new 'energy saving' gadget really essential and using any available hot water in the hot water tank rather than an instantaneous electrically powered device will all help. Heating the house up slowly is much more efficient than turning the boiler on full power and expecting immediate results, similarly the ability to zone areas of the house into areas of different temperature patterns will reduce costs and at the same time increase user comfort. Getting used to simply switching something off when it's not in use will also help significantly. Energy is an expensive commodity who's irresponsible use ultimately adds to our problem of global warming and the ensuing environmental affects, it is up to all of us, no matter what our resources, to do our best to curb this trend.

For further information on ways to save energy at home contact **IRISH ENERGY CENTRE GLASNEVIN, DUBLIN 9 Tel: (01) 8369080,** Who will be happy to advise.

We also wish to acknowledge their assistance in the provision of some technical data used in this article.

SECTION B: DESIGNS 2031-2060
Floor Areas over 1800 square feet

 Page86-2031

 Page88-2032

 Page90-2033

Page91-2034

Page92-2035

Page96-2036

 Page99-2037

Page100-2038

Page102-2039

Page104-2040

Page106-2041

Page108-2042

 Page110-2043

Page120-2044

Page122-2045

Page124-2046

Page126-2047

Page128-2048

 Page130-2049

Page132-2050

Page134-2051

Page136-2052

Page138-2053

Page140-2054

 Page142-2055

Page144-2056

Page146-2057

Page148-2058

Page150-2059

Page152-2060

85

Front Perspective

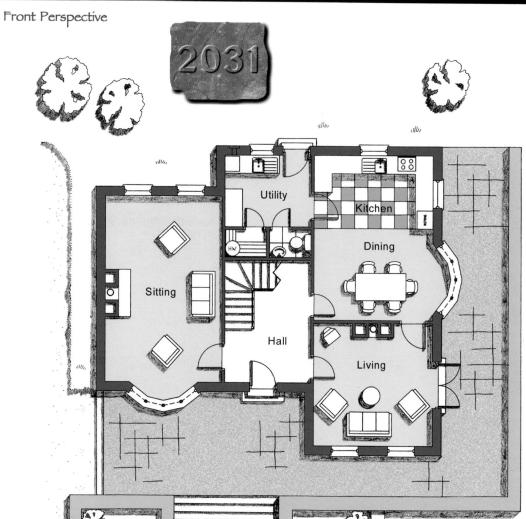

2031

Utility

Kitchen

Dining

HW

Sitting

Hall

Living

Ground Floor Plan

For **Construction Costs**
See Page 154 & 155

First Floor Plan

Four Bedrooms.
Kitchen\Dining - 13' 01"x17' 08"
Living - 13' 01"x13' 01"
Sitting - 13' 05"x20' 00"
Bed 1 - 13' 01"x13' 01"
Bed 2 -13' 01"x12' 07"
Bed 3 - 13' 05"x9' 11"
Bed 4 - 13' 05"x8' 09"
Overall Length - 38' 03"
Overall Width - 33' 02"
Floor Area - 1804 sq. ft.

This has proved a very popular design as a result of two simple principles:
1) Good planning, the rooms radiate out from the central core of hall and staircase which results in easy circulation of the dwelling for the occupants.
2) An elegant facade that employs traditional, well proportioned windows all round.

View towards living room patio doors and dining room bay window

Front perspective

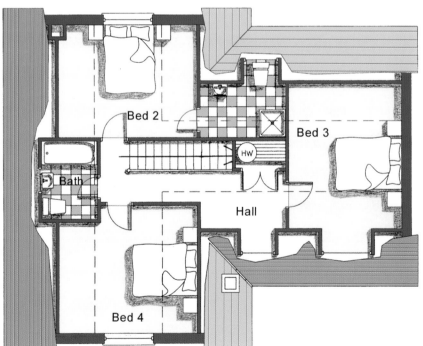

Floor Plan

2032

A well proportioned one and a half storey dwelling defined by a projecting gable and square bay to front left.

As with several of the designs in this book a study\office has been incorporated. This is a feature we believe will become more and more prevalent as the new century progresses.

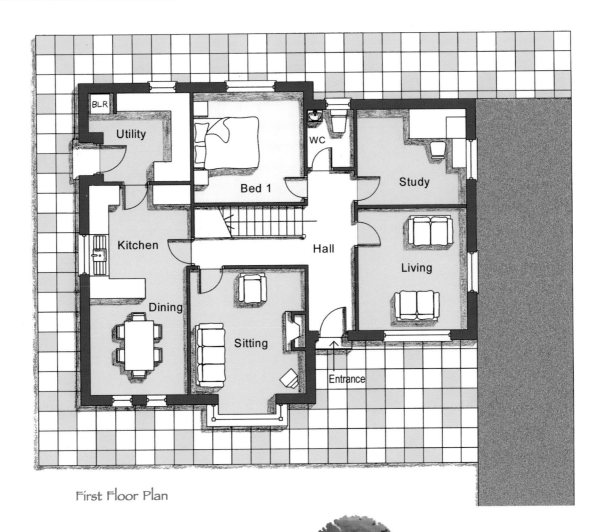

First Floor Plan

Four Bedrooms.
Kitchen\Dining - 9' 10"x19' 00"
Living - 11' 04"x12' 01"
Sitting - 11' 10"x12' 06"
Study - 11' 04"x9' 06"
Bed 1 - 11' 04"x11' 00"
Bed 2 -14' 01"x11' 00"
Bed 3 - 10' 08"x14' 01"
Bed 4 - 14' 01"x12' 06"
Overall Length - 40' 08"
Overall Width - 34' 02"
Floor Area - 1801 sq. ft.

View from front left showing alternative finishes:
rendered walls with vertical timber cladding to dormers.

For **Construction Costs**
See Page 154 & 155

Front Perspective

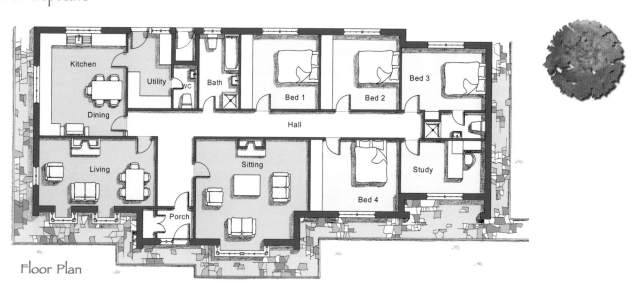

Floor Plan

2033

Four Bedrooms.
Kitchen\Dining - 14' 01"x16' 02"
Living - 19' 00"x10' 08"
Sitting - 18' 07"x15' 08"
Bed 1 - 12' 10"x11' 09"
Bed 2 -12' 09"x11' 09"
Bed 3 - 13' 08"x9' 09"
Bed 4 - 14' 03"x11' 04"
Study - 13' 08"x8' 05"
Overall Length - 74' 08"
Overall Width - 35' 11"
Floor Area - 2064 sq. ft.

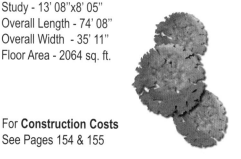

For **Construction Costs**
See Pages 154 & 155

This large, elegant single storey house could be finished in either brick or render and is similar in scale and plan form to design 2034 (opposite).
The half hipped roof and georgian glazing help to complete a rustic feel.

Rear Perspective

View from front garden

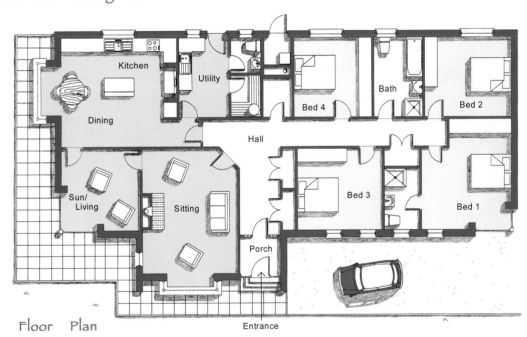

Floor Plan

Entrance

Four Bedrooms.
Kitchen - 17' 09"x15' 09"
Living\Sun - 12' 02"x11' 10"
Sitting - 14' 05"x18' 01"
Bed 1 - 13' 01"x10' 00"
Bed 2 -13' 04"x11' 06"
Bed 3 - 12' 11"x11' 10"
Bed 4 - 11' 10"x11' 06"
Overall Length - 74' 01"
Overall Width - 37' 09"
Floor Area - 2082 sq. ft.

2034

Side View towards sun lounge\living room

A large single storey dwelling with a shallow hipped roof to reduce impact.
A notable feature of this design is the corner glazing to both the sun lounge and bedroom 1 which work well in conjunction with the two square bay projections to the sitting and dining spaces.

For **Construction Costs** See Pages 154 & 155

Copyright 2000 Plan-A-Home

View from front garden towards entrance

2035

Four Bedrooms.
Kitchen - 13' 08"x11' 06"
Dining - 5' 11"x14' 05"
Living - 13' 08"x11' 06"
Bed 1 - 9' 10"x19' 08"
Bed 2 -14' 00"x16' 01"
Bed 3 - 9' 06"x11' 10"
Bed 4 - 13' 02"x9' 06"
Overall Length - 45' 03"
Overall Width - 47' 07"
Floor Area - 1812 sq. ft.

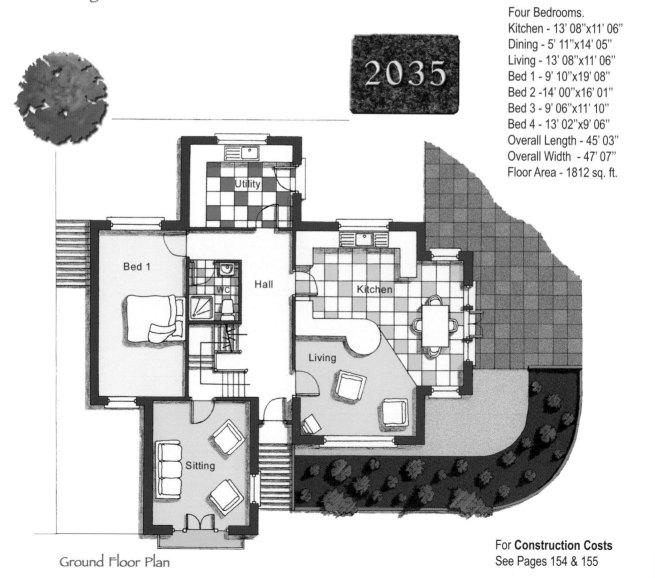

Ground Floor Plan

For **Construction Costs**
See Pages 154 & 155

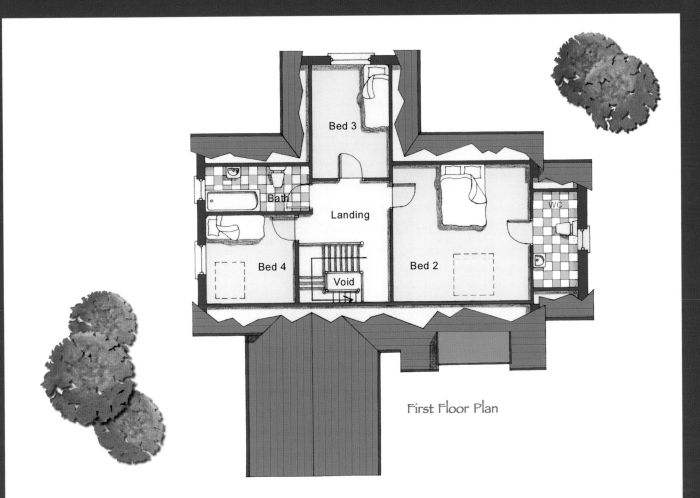

Bed 3

Bath

Landing

Bed 4

Void

Bed 2

WC

First Floor Plan

This design is illustrated on a declining site and using the addition of a garage under to use up the gradient and give a split-level feature to the sitting room. Likewise this design would also lend itself to an inclining site by omitting the garage. The main feature of this design is the large spacious open plan kitchen/dining/living area suited to those families who prefer to dine and rest in the same area. A large spacious utility helping to reduce demands on the open plan kitchen. The bedroom proportions are obviously adaptable depending on individual requirements.

View towards rear

Sar Ghlan Teoranta Advanced Wastewater Projects

Meenmore
Dungloe County Donegal
Phone:074 95 61836
Fax: 074 95 61837
Email sarghlanteo@eircom.net

Low cost installation

Easy access to every component of the system

No moving parts to wear out

24 Month warranty

Low running costs

No filters to clog up

Low cost maintenance

Protects the environment

ECO-FLOW TANK

Model EFT2003

Advanced Wastewater Treatment Plant

(One Piece)

Innovation Not Imitation

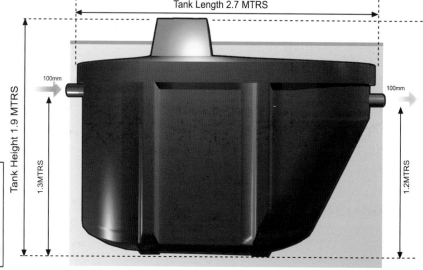

Tank Length 2.7 MTRS

Tank Height 1.9 MTRS

1.3MTRS

100mm

100mm

1.2MTRS

IRISH AGRÉMENT BOARD

Building Product Certification Pending

OUR SUN

The Ultimate Source of Energy For The Earth

With Solterra You Have It Available
To Heat Your Home And Hot Water
All Year Round

SOLTERRA
Geoenergy
Solutions

Dunstar Ltd
Phone: 023-35165   Fax: 023-35174
e-mail: dunstar@eircom.net
Web: www.solterra.ie
1, Kent Road, Clonakilty, Co. Cork

Front Perspective

2036

This is a popular cottage design. Its facade is simple, elegant and symmetrical and is adaptable to various finishes or a combination of finishes as illustrated above and on the next page.

An alternative floor plan has been provided and highlights the fact that all plans within this book can be adapted to suit the needs of the client.

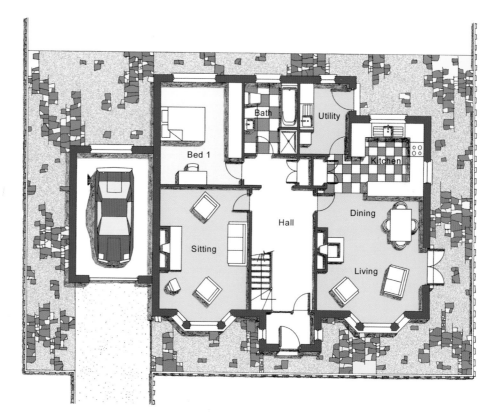

Ground Floor Plan

For **Construction Costs**
See Pages 154 & 155

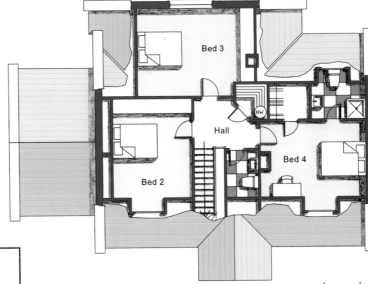

First Floor Plan

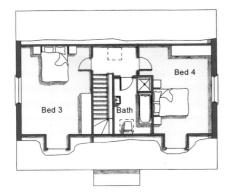

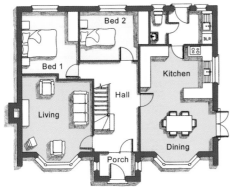

Four Bedrooms.
Overall Length - 50' 10''
Overall Width - 37' 01''
Living\Dining - 14' 09''x15' 05''
Kitchen - 14' 09''x9' 10''
Sitting - 12' 07''x16' 04''
Bed 1 - 11' 05''x13' 09''
Bed 2 -11' 01''x13' 04''
Bed 3 - 15' 02''x11' 09''
Bed 4 - 14' 09''x10' 02''
Floor Area - 1828 sq. ft.

Alternative floor plans
(without garage)
(floor areas not given)

Similar view but with stone cladding to gables

97

Think Roof, Think Thrutone

Tegral provide a range of highly durable smooth or textured roof slates in a variety of shapes and imaginative colours. These are Irish slates made to meet Irish weather conditions with guarantees backed by over 60 year's experience. There is Nationwide availability from leading Builders Providers and Merchants. When you need a roof over your head it's comforting to know that Tegral has it covered.

Tegral Building Products Ltd. Athy, Co. Kildare
Tel: 0507 31316 Fax: 0507 38637 email: info@tegral.ie website: http//www.tegral.ie

Front Perspective

A simple traditional form, using roof windows and gable windows to light first floor which is a cost effective way of developing your attic. The layout obviously suits a site with a southerly view yet a northern entrance. The kitchen/utility arrangement could be interchanged dependent on what site has to offer in terms of view & sunlight. The simplistic design & raised barges achieve a neat sharp appearance.

Five Bedrooms.
Kitchen\Dining - 10' 06"x15' 11"
Living - 16' 05"x11' 10"
Bed 1 - 11' 02"x13' 09"
Bed 2 -11' 02"x11' 07"
Bed 3 - 10' 10"x9' 06"
Bed 4 - 11' 02"x14' 06"
Bed 5 - 11' 03"x14' 06"
Study - 9' 09"x8' 03"
Overall Length - 47' 07"
Overall Width - 27' 08"
Floor Area - 1826 sq. ft.

2037

Ground Floor Plan

Rear Perspective

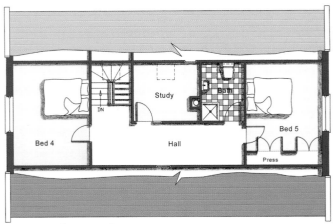

First Floor Plan

For Construction Costs See Pages 154 & 155

Front Perspective

Elevation A

2038

Four Bedrooms.
Kitchen - 16' 05''x16' 05''
Dining - 17' 01''x11' 02''
Living - 17' 01''x14' 09''
Sitting - 17' 01''x17' 01''
Bed 1 - 15' 09''x11' 02''
Bed 2 -17' 01''x10' 10''
Bed 3 - 14' 05''x22' 00''
Bed 4 - 12' 06''x19' 00''
Overall Length - 59' 08''
Overall Width - 62' 04''
Floor Area - 2734 sq. ft.

Elevation B

For **Construction Costs**
See Pages 154 & 155

Elevation A
▽

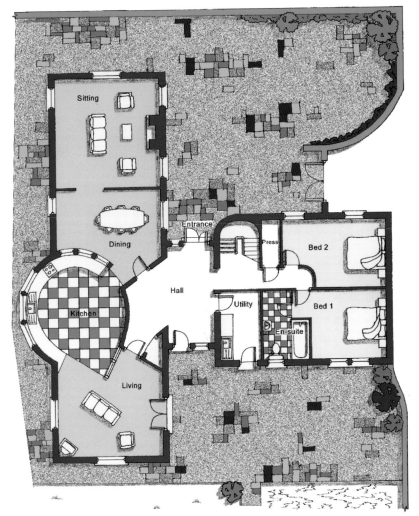

Sitting

Dining

Entrance

Press

Bed 2

◁ Elevation B

Hall

Kitchen

Utility

Bed 1

En-suite

Living

Ground Floor Plan

The formal geometry of this house belies the fluid spatial relation between the kitchen, living and sitting rooms. Your passage through the house is guided by an arrangement of obliquely aligned walls. The glazed hall wall divides the ground floor living and sleeping accommodation. The simple form of the house and the proportion of wall to window offers a traditional cottage feel masking a free-flowing modern interior.

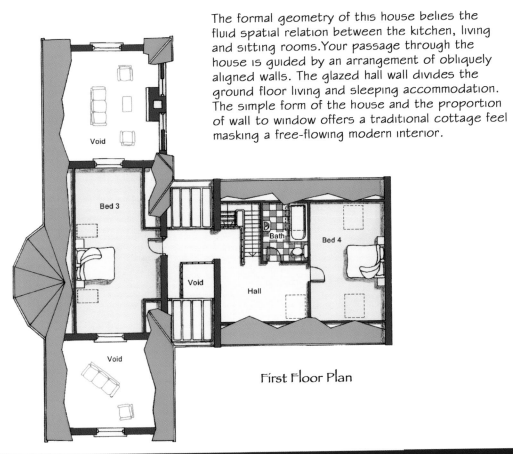

Void

Bed 3

Bed 4

Bath

Void

Hall

Void

First Floor Plan

View towards living room with main entrance to right

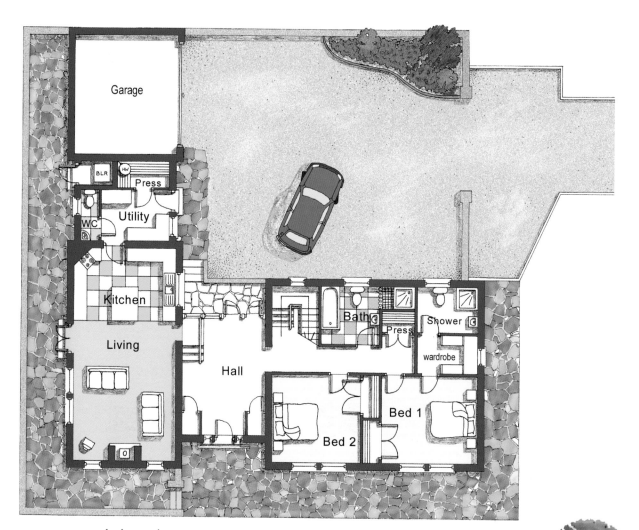

Ground Floor Plan

For Construction Costs
See Pages 154 & 155

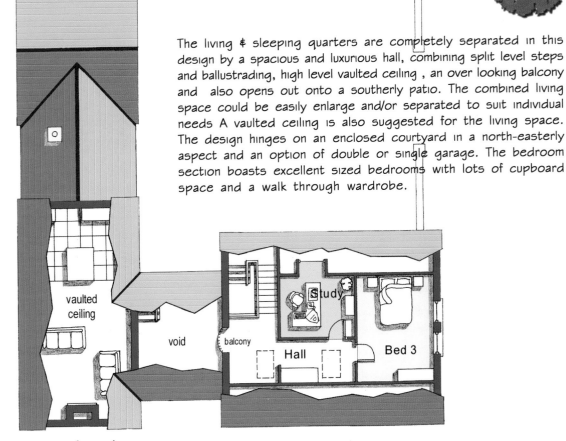

The living & sleeping quarters are completely separated in this design by a spacious and luxurious hall, combining split level steps and ballustrading, high level vaulted ceiling , an over looking balcony and also opens out onto a southerly patio. The combined living space could be easily enlarge and/or separated to suit individual needs A vaulted ceiling is also suggested for the living space. The design hinges on an enclosed courtyard in a north-easterly aspect and an option of double or single garage. The bedroom section boasts excellent sized bedrooms with lots of cupboard space and a walk through wardrobe.

vaulted ceiling

void

balcony

Study

Bed 3

Hall

First Floor Plan

View into rear courtyard

2029

Three Bedrooms.
Kitchen - 14' 03"x9' 10"
Living - 14' 03"x18' 08"
Bed 1 - 13' 02"x11' 06"
Bed 2 -12' 02"x11' 10"
Bed 3 -14' 09"x10' 06"
Study -8' 06"x10' 06"
Overall Length - 59' 00"
Overall Width - 43' 08"
Floor Area - 1850 sq. ft.

View from front garden towards porch entrance

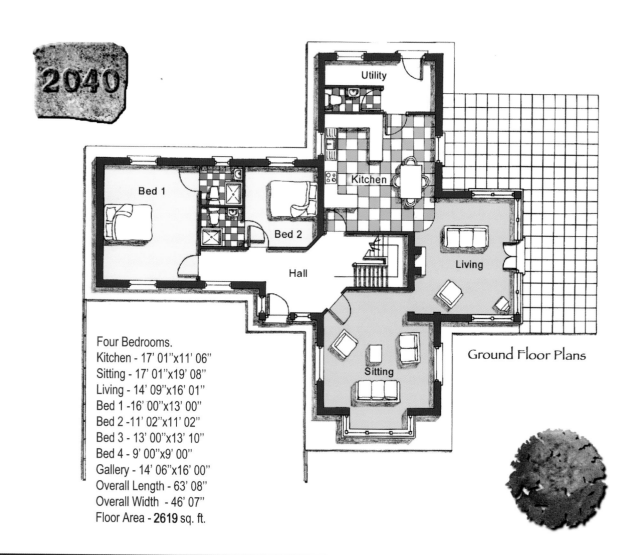

2040

Four Bedrooms.
Kitchen - 17' 01''x11' 06''
Sitting - 17' 01''x19' 08''
Living - 14' 09''x16' 01''
Bed 1 -16' 00''x13' 00''
Bed 2 -11' 02''x11' 02''
Bed 3 - 13' 00''x13' 10''
Bed 4 - 9' 00''x9' 00''
Gallery - 14' 06''x16' 00''
Overall Length - 63' 08''
Overall Width - 46' 07''
Floor Area - **2619** sq. ft.

Ground Floor Plans

For **Construction Costs**
See Pages 154 & 155

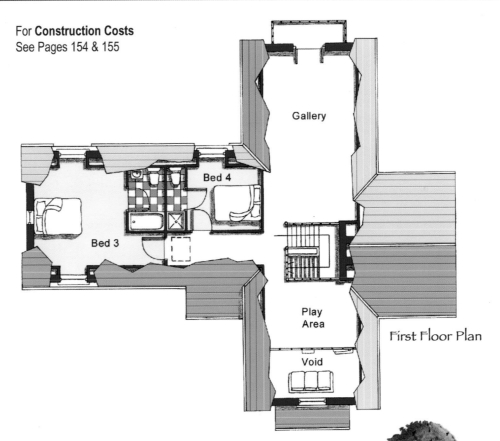

Gallery

Bed 4

Bed 3

Play Area

Void

First Floor Plan

Preferably suited to a north facing site where privacy can be retained to the south and west. This house has generous living spaces, interlinked to offer the option of open plan or independent spaces depending on lifestyle. A centrally located stair, top lit by velux windows, leads onto a spacious open landing/gallery which could be altered to room spaces if required. Features include partially vaulted ceiling over sitting room, vaulted conservatory styled living room and external balcony. As with all plans, this design offers versatility for alternative layouts.

Front view towards main entrance

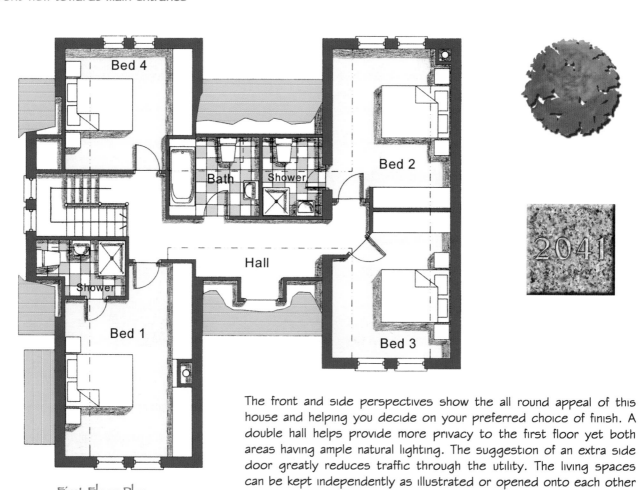

First Floor Plan

The front and side perspectives show the all round appeal of this house and helping you decide on your preferred choice of finish. A double hall helps provide more privacy to the first floor yet both areas having ample natural lighting. The suggestion of an extra side door greatly reduces traffic through the utility. The living spaces can be kept independently as illustrated or opened onto each other depending on clients needs. The scaled furniture clearly shows the spaciousness of all four bedrooms.

Ground Floor Plan

View from driveway towards sitting room bay . Shown with a render finish

Four Bedrooms.
Kitchen - 12' 06"x13' 01"
Dining - 15' 03"x11' 05"
Living - 11' 06"x18' 03"
Sitting - 12' 06"x15' 09"
Bed 1 - 10' 06"x18' 04"
Bed 2 -11' 06"x15' 00"
Bed 3 - 11' 06"x13' 09"
Bed 4 - 10' 06"x11' 10"
Overall Length - 42' 04"
Overall Width - 40' 04"
Floor Area - 2200 sq. ft.

For **Construction Costs**
See Pages 154 & 155

Front perspective

Four Bedrooms.
Kitchen/Dining - 12' 10''x14' 09''
Sitting - 12' 10''x15' 09''
Living - 14' 09''x16' 05''
Bed 1 - 9' 10''x16' 05''
Bed 2 - 9' 10''x11' 02''
Bed 3 - 18' 04''x13' 02''
Bed 4 - 10' 02''x13' 02''
Overall Length - 47' 03''
Overall Width - 43' 04''
Floor Area - 1810 sq. ft.

2042

Bed 3

Bath

Bed 4

Hall

Void

Living

First Floor Plan

For **Construction Costs**
See Pages 154 & 155

Ground Floor Plan

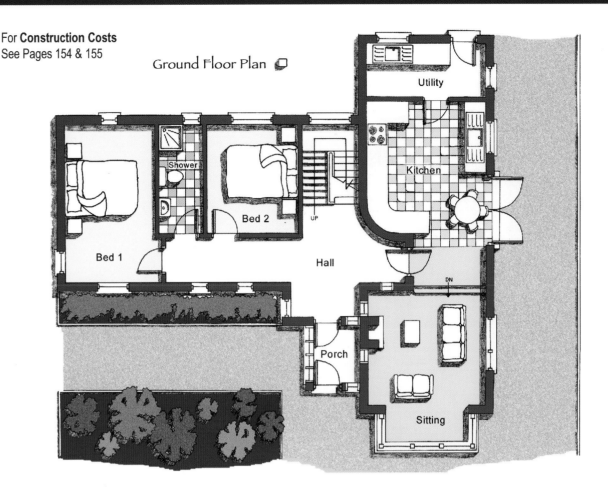

Utility

Kitchen

Shower

Bed 2

Bed 1

Hall

UP

DN

Porch

Sitting

This four bedroom dormer combines the best elements of traditional planning with contemporary standards of design. Drawing from the cottages of old, the plan is essentially a single room deep, allowing rooms to be double aspect. The design features a traditional, combined kitchen/living area, yet at the same time, skillfully incorporates modern touches such as the open space over the dining area, overlooked by the first floor living room.

Rear Perspective

Front Perspective

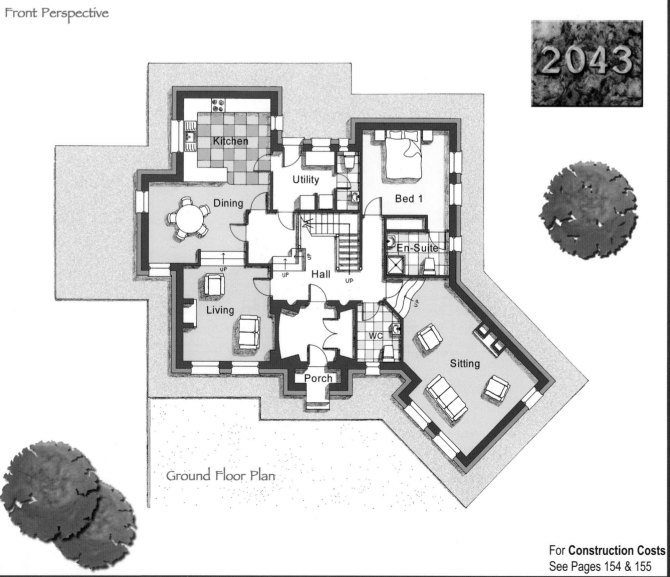

2043

Kitchen

Utility

Bed 1

Dining

En-Suite

Hall

Living

WC

Sitting

Porch

Ground Floor Plan

For **Construction Costs**
See Pages 154 & 155

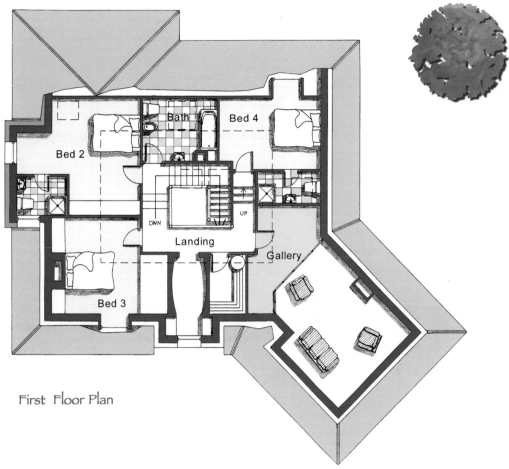

First Floor Plan

This highly distinctive, large four bedroom dormer house is ideally suited to large suburban sites.

As well as boasting generously proportioned rooms throughout, it features a ground floor master bedroom, a gallery providing a dramatic view overlooking the sitting room and a grand staircase to the rooms above.

A similar view but with a traditional render finish

Four Bedrooms.
Living - 12' 06"x13' 0"
Kitchen - 12' 06"x11' 06"
Dining - 13' 11"x11' 02"
Sitting - 14' 09"x18' 03"
Bed 1 - 12' 06"x11' 08"
Bed 2 -12' 06"x13' 11"
Bed 3 - 12' 06"x13' 00"
Bed 4 - 14' 05"x9' 08"
Overall Length - 41' 04"
Overall Width - 39' 05"
Floor Area - 2568 sq. ft.

Gardening: A New Lawn

A New Lawn

The grass on your lawn can come from seed or turf. Sowing seed is the cheapest form of lawn production whilst laying turf is quicker but much more expensive. If the area of lawn is not very large it may be worth considering turf.

Step one

If you have moved into a new house the site for your new lawn is probably an overgrown area of weeds and builder's rubble.

Note: on no account must the subsoil from foundation digging be spread about the area of intended lawn, unless any existing top soil is first stacked at a convenient point. Some or all of the subsoil may be used to fill large hollows, if this is not necessary the subsoil must be carried away and dumped. When the area has been roughly cleared, before any work on the lawn can begin, all pathways and kerb edgings must be laid.

At this point it is necessary to consider hedges or wooden fences. For proper and even hedge growth, it is necessary to dig a trench 2ft deep and 3ft wide.

This can be accomplished very easily if you hire a machine for a few hours. If, in the course of digging the trench, the soil proves to be of poor quality it is best to backfill the trench with good quality soil, treading down as you do so. It is not necessary to plant hedges at this time, the trench can be simply be marked out. With regard to wooden fencing you can pick your own design - the important thing is to set all upright posts in concrete.

Step two

Grade the site: (Omit this step if levelling is not requried). A lawn does not have to be level, a slight slope will help drainage, but must be free from bumps and hollows. Gentle undulations are acceptable in a large lawn but are out of place in a small one. To grade a site with major bumps and hollows first remove topsoil and stack at a convenient point, all alterations must be made with subsoil. When a desired level has been obtained, replace the topsoil. On no account should subsoil be brought to the surface. The topsoil layer must have a minimum depth of 6 inches.

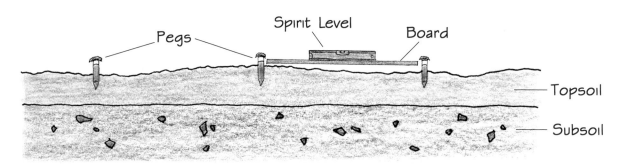

Diagram 1

Gardens: A New Lawn

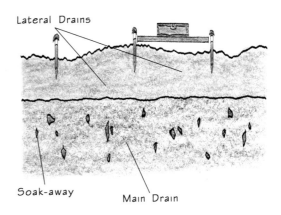

Lateral Drains

Soak-away   Main Drain

Diagram 2

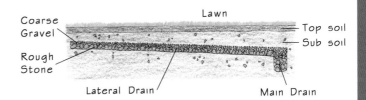

Coarse Gravel — Rough Stone — Lateral Drain — Lawn — Top soil — Sub soil — Main Drain

To obtain a level surface: you will need wooden pegs, a wooden board 7ft long, and a spirit level. On each wooden peg paint a line 3 inches from the top. First rough level the soil by eye. Then knock in a peg so its mark is just above the soil. Take the board with the spirit level on top of it and place it against the mark on the peg holding the board so that it is level. Then 6ft along knock in another peg so its mark is also level with the board. Continue to do this until the ground is adequately covered with pegs. Then level up the soil to the painted marks on the pegs. For practical reasons this really only applies to a fairly small lawn.

If soil has already been spread on your lawn, it will be necessary to deal with weed growth. If soil has a cover of weed growth, spray with Glyphosate or Paraquat. When weed growth has died down, cultivate soil. A second flush of weed growth will take place and it will be necessary to treat with weedkiller again. If soil has been freshly spread on the lawn, no weeds are in evidence, and it is the correct time to seed the lawn – **Do So**. If the time is not right to seed the lawn, level soil and cultivate, this will encourage weed growth, then treat with weedkiller.

This exercise is known as **fallowing the soil**. The purpose of this is to get rid of dormant weed seeds. Fallowing the site should ideally take place over a period of 2 to 3 months before the lawn is seeded. The best time for sowing lawn seed is between mid August and mid September, the next best is April. The best time to lay turf is October to February and the next best is March to April. Do not lay turf in frosty weather.

A simple drainage system (see Diagram 2) will be of value if water tends to remain on the surface after heavy rain. To do this, dig a main drain on the lowest side of the site 2 to 3 ft deep, at one end of this drain a soakaway may have to be costructed. Run lateral or side drains into main drain, spaced about 8 ft apart with a slight slope, fill with rough stone and top off with 3 inches of coarse gravel. <u>Note</u>: lateral drains at their highest points, need to be 12 inches below ground level. The minimum depth of soil to cover all drains must be 6 inches.

Step three

Dig the site: If the area of the lawn is small it may be possible to dig by hand: a fork is easier to use than a spade. Dig to a depth of 9 inches or less if topsoil is shallow. Do not bring up the subsoil. For a large area, hire a mechanical cultivator.

Gardening: A New Lawn

When the area has been dug over, leave to settle for a week or so, when weather conditions allow rough rake the area. Use a coarse toothed rake (not plastic) moving the rake backwards and forwards in a scuffing motion. As you rake this will have the effect of rough levelling the area. Do not try to get a finished level at this stage. This can be done later when the soil is graded to a finer texture. Leave for some days in rough raked condition, as weather will expose stones and help to break down lumps of soil. Starting at one end of the site rake stones, rubbish etc. into rows. When removing rows of rubble do not use a shovel, as you tend to remove topsoil with rubble, use instead a mutli-tined fork, a potato fork is ideal. If this fork is not available then you will have to use a shovel, taking care to remove as little soil as possible. Re-rake area with a fine toothed rake levelling as you go, again you will have a finer grade of rubble to remove. As you rake, the soil will consolidate, helping to form the seed bed. The ideal seed bed is firm to walk on with an inch or two of crumbly soil on top.

Do not use a garden roller to consolidate the soil, air pockets are often left, and bumps are not levelled, but made worse. Also, on certain soils, rolling will cause soil compaction. When you have reached this stage, the lawn is now ready for sowing. Sow lawn seed at the rate of 1° oz per square yard.

To sow lawn seed evenly it is best to hire or buy a fertiliser spreader, it will have settings to sow lawn seed. Before you sow seed it will be necessary to apply a pre-seed fertiliser, at the rate of 2oz per square yard.

This can be applied immediately before sowing lawn seed. When fertiliser and seed have been sown, lightly rake the whole area with a spring-tined rake, (a leaf rake will do) to partly cover seeds, do not bury seed or germination will be patchy. Seedlings will appear 7 - 21 days after sowing depending on the weather. Do not walk on seeded lawn. Any damage by birds, cats, dogs etc is best left as it can be repaired when the grass is an inch or two high. When the grass is 3 inches high the lawn can have its first cut. Only the top inch of grass should be removed. Thereafter cut grass as normal. Never cut a lawn below one inch, as this encourages moss, and bare patches on lawns. If the weather turns dry when the lawn is sown do not water, you will not be able to apply enough water lightly.

Heavy watering causes seed to be washed out of position or washed away, it also causes soil to split open in dry weather causing even more water loss. Do not worry about birds. Seed eating birds do not dig for seed. Fertilise your lawn two or three times per year, cut grass twice each week if possible at height of growing season. If you decide to lay turf, lawn area should be prepared as for seeding. If shrubs and trees are not already in-situ grass down entire area, as cutting the grass keeps the future tree and shrub areas clean and weed free. A new lawn must not be treated for weeds until one year old.

Note: A well made lawn with a little care will last a lifetime.

GARDENS

Formal Garden

Formal gardens must be laid out to rigid designs. A garden of this type allows for many different planting styles. In formal beds cut from the lawn, near the house, seasonal bedding plants would be used. In the larger flower borders herbacious perennials might be employed, while groups of bulbs could be set between the shrubs in the boundary borders.

Informal Garden

There are no hard or fast rules as to how an informal garden should be laid out. It could in fact be laid out as a cottage garden, old fashioned plants all crowded together, with scent and butterflies filling the air. Everywhere there should be an informal air ; rockeries, naturalised bulbs, hardy perennials planted in a jumble of colours, and shrubs planted in groups rather than straight lines.

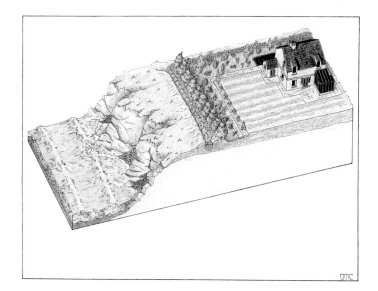

Seaside Garden

Seaside gardens are exposed to salt laden winds. Evergreen hedges and shrubs are best for use as windbreaks. If space allows, use evergreen trees, Austrian Pine or Pinus Contorta. Carnations and Pinks are among the best flowers planted en masse.

A sheltered alcove with a seat , at the end of the garden, can be a restful haven.

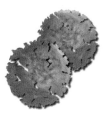

Awkward Shaped Garden

Corner sites or awkward shaped gardens offer special problems in planning. Plots with irregular boundaries can either be treated throughout in an informal manner, or a section can be cut out for formal treatment. The remaining corners can be planted with decorative shrubs and trees. Where formal and informal are combined in one garden, the more formal treatment should be nearer the house, where straight lines and angles are already in existence.

Childrens' Garden

A garden such as this is ideal for youngsters, both for playing and outdoor meals. It includes a slide, very shallow pool, sand pit, (washed gravel is much cleaner than sand), swing, flower bed and a paved area. A high wall gives protection from prevailing wind.

All these features can be included in an area about 40ft square.

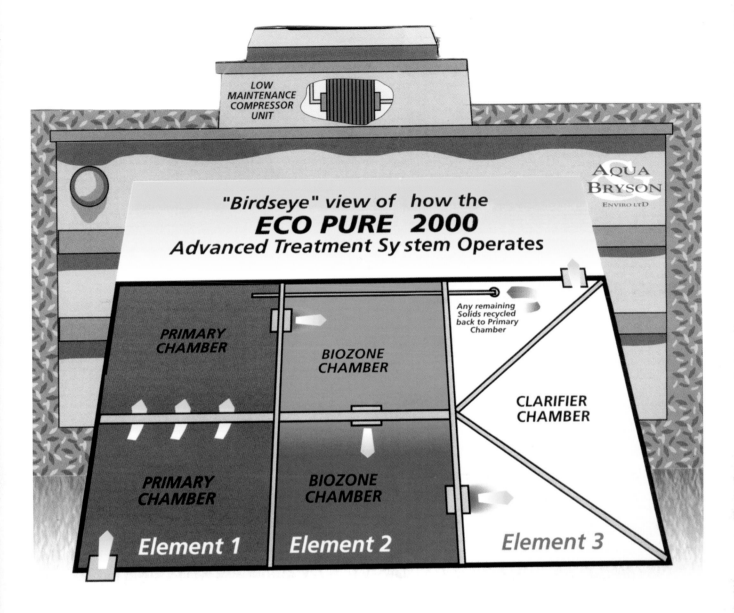

"Birdseye" view of how the
ECO PURE 2000
Advanced Treatment System Operates

PRIMARY CHAMBER

BIOZONE CHAMBER

Any remaining Solids recycled back to Primary Chamber

CLARIFIER CHAMBER

PRIMARY CHAMBER

BIOZONE CHAMBER

Element 1

Element 2

Element 3

We serve all areas be they:

- Residential Housing
- Nursing and Retirement Homes
- Schools and Colleges
- Hotel and Leisure Facilities
- Offices
- Commercial developments
- Caravan Parks

ECO PURE 2000
Sewage Treatment System

AQUA & BRYSON
ENVIRO LTD

**Rathforker,
Donegal Town, Co. Donegal.
Tel: 00353 (0)73 22077
Fax: 00353 (0)73 22429
e-mail: aquaenviromental@tinet.ie**

CALLSAVE 1850 - 220770

View from front garden towards porch entrance

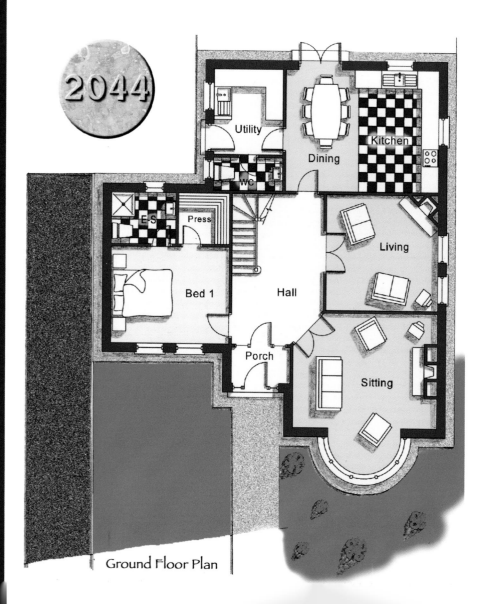

2044

Utility

Kitchen

Dining

WC

E S

Press

Living

Bed 1

Hall

Porch

Sitting

Four Bedrooms.
Kitchen/Dining - 17' 05"x13' 02"
Living - 12' 08"x12' 08"
Sitting - 16' 05"x17' 07"
Bed 1 -13' 03"x11' 06"
Bed 2 -13' 03"x16' 05"
Bed 3 - 16' 04"x13' 02"
Bed 4 - 16' 05"x12' 06"
Overall Length - 39' 01"
Overall Width - 46' 04"
Floor Area - 2123 sq. ft.

Ground Floor Plan

For **Construction Costs**
See Pages 154 & 155

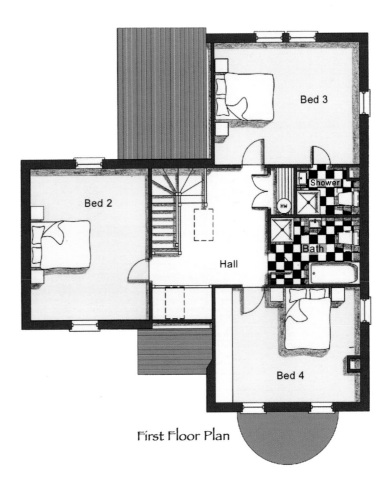

Bed 2

Bed 3

Shower

HW

Bath

Hall

Bed 4

First Floor Plan

This model was initially designed for a south/
easterly aspect, with the kitchen and living room
maximizing the natural light, a large bay window
in the sitting area availing of the evening sun,
and the master bedroom availing of the rising sun.
A semi vaulted hall gives an impression of space,
which applies to every room in the house.

View towards rear of house

View from garden

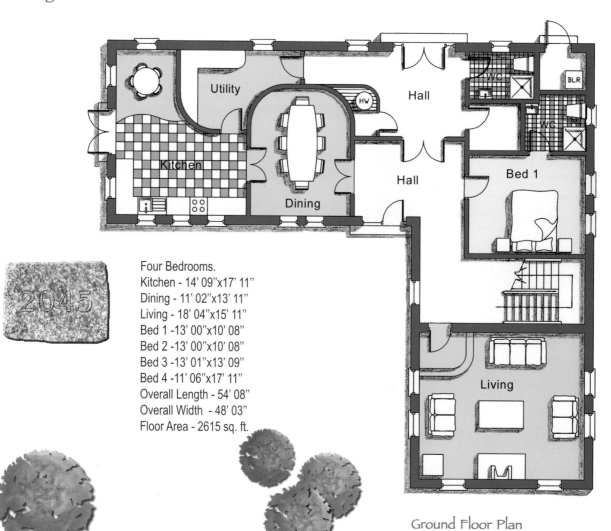

Four Bedrooms.
Kitchen - 14' 09"x17' 11"
Dining - 11' 02"x13' 11"
Living - 18' 04"x15' 11"
Bed 1 -13' 00"x10' 08"
Bed 2 -13' 00"x10' 08"
Bed 3 -13' 01"x13' 09"
Bed 4 -11' 06"x17' 11"
Overall Length - 54' 08"
Overall Width - 48' 03"
Floor Area - 2615 sq. ft.

Ground Floor Plan

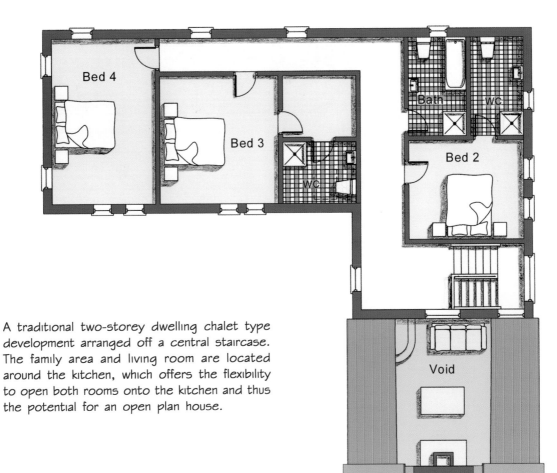

Bed 4

Bed 3

Bath

WC

WC

Bed 2

Void

A traditional two-storey dwelling chalet type development arranged off a central staircase. The family area and living room are located around the kitchen, which offers the flexibility to open both rooms onto the kitchen and thus the potential for an open plan house.

First Floor Plan

View along driveway towards front entrance

For Construction Costs
See Pages 154 & 155

123

View from garden towards living, dinig and kitchen

The elements of this house have been arranged in a manner similar to the house and outbuildings of a traditional farmyard setting. The house is provided with ample storage space for each bedroom and general storage on the ground floor.

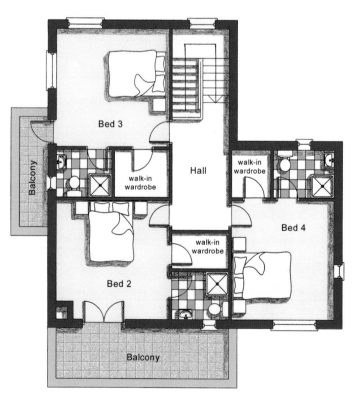

Bed 3

Balcony

walk-in wardrobe

Hall

walk-in wardrobe

Bed 4

2046

walk-in wardrobe

Bed 2

Balcony

First Floor Plan

For **Construction Costs**
See Pages 154 & 155

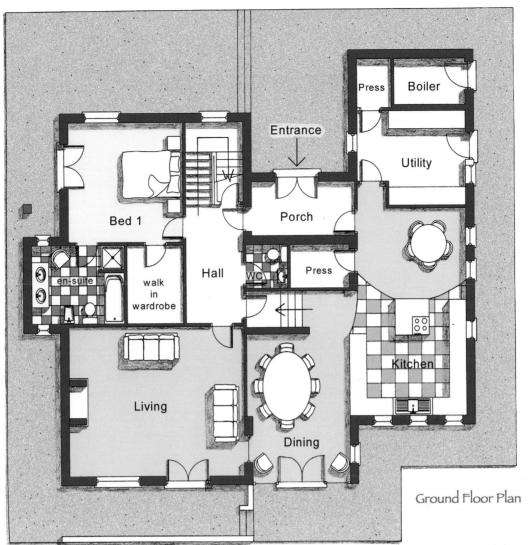

Entrance

Press | Boiler

Utility

Bed 1

Porch

en-suite | walk in wardrobe | Hall | WC | Press

Living

Dining

Kitchen

Ground Floor Plan

Four Bedrooms.
Kitchen - 12' 06"x22' 07"
Living - 20' 00"x16' 05"
Dining - 11' 02"x15' 06"
Bed 1 - 13' 01"x13' 01"

Bed 2 - 13' 01"x13' 01"
Bed 3 - 13' 01"x13' 01"
Bed 4 - 11' 10"x13' 03"
Overall Length - 51' 10"
Overall Width - 47' 07"
Floor Area - 2585 sq. ft.

View towards main entrance with the balcony to Bed 3 on the right

View towards main entrance and sitting room bay

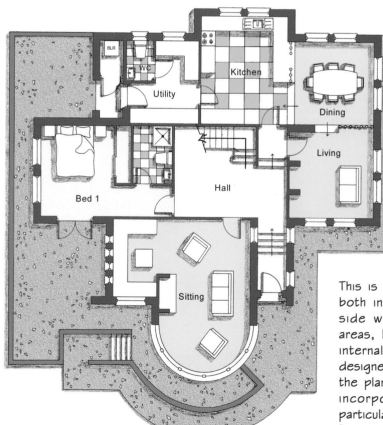

Ground Floor Plan

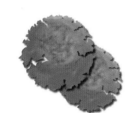

2047

This is a very desirable home, lots of character both inside and out. Designed onto a sloping side with living spaces having deep glazing areas, helping to make the outside part of the internal space. Many of the rooms have been designed with this in mind so a closer study of the plan may highlight areas that could be even incorporated into a different design. This particular design has its hall and landing lighted from roof windows on the landing vault ceiling. Split levels are also a distinguishing feature of this design.

126

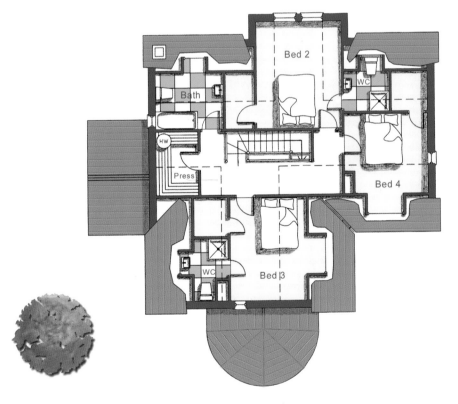

Four Bedrooms.
Overall Length - 47' 03''
Overall Width - 48' 06''
Living - 11' 06''x12' 02''
Kitchen - 11' 10''x14' 01''
Dining - 10' 10''x11' 10''
Sitting - 10' 08''x18' 08''
Bed 1 - 12' 10''x11' 10''
Bed 2 -11' 10''x14' 01''
Bed 3 - 10' 06''x13' 08''
Bed 4 - 11' 06''x10' 06''
Floor Area - 2218 sq. ft.

First Floor Plan

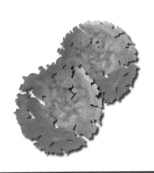

For **Construction Costs**
See Pages 154 & 155

Front view of lower ground level towards garage and main entrance

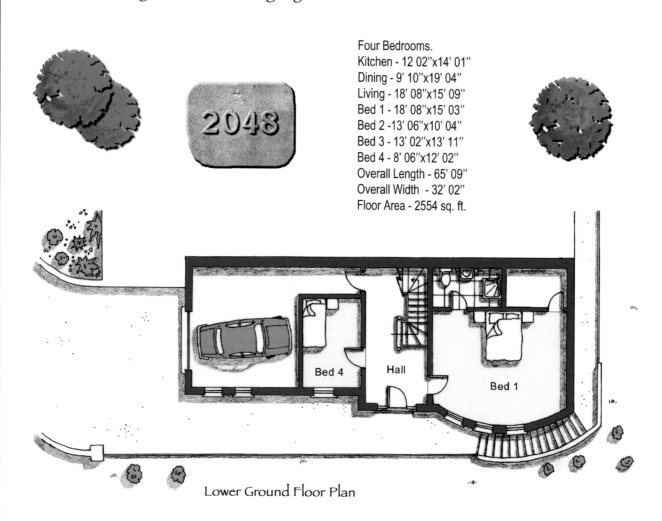

Four Bedrooms.
Kitchen - 12 02"x14' 01"
Dining - 9' 10"x19' 04"
Living - 18' 08"x15' 09"
Bed 1 - 18' 08"x15' 03"
Bed 2 -13' 06"x10' 04"
Bed 3 - 13' 02"x13' 11"
Bed 4 - 8' 06"x12' 02"
Overall Length - 65' 09"
Overall Width - 32' 02"
Floor Area - 2554 sq. ft.

2048

Bed 4
Hall
Bed 1

Lower Ground Floor Plan

For **Construction Costs**
See Pages 154 & 155

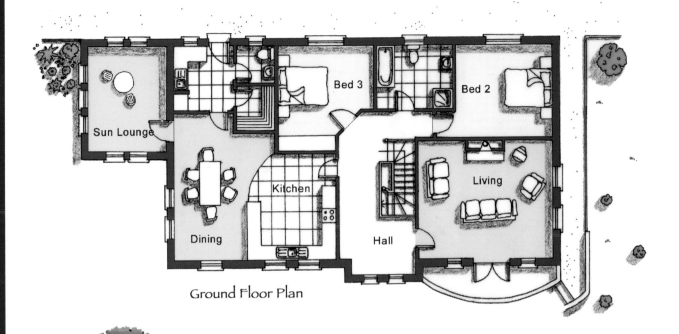

Ground Floor Plan

Ideally suited to a split-level or steeply sloping site but could
be altered to work as a two storey house on a flat site.
Entrance is via the lower ground floor and into the main hall from
where a staircase leads up to all the main living areas.
The kitchen and dining room are designed as open plan, although
a separating wall could be added if preferred. The living room features
an open balcony which is located over the curved wall of the master
bedroom.

Rear view showing entrance to utility room

View from front garden towards porch entrance

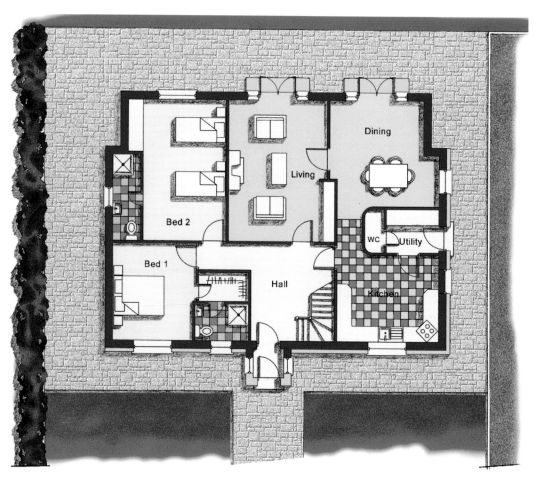

Ground Floor Plan

For **Construction Costs**
See Pages 154 & 155

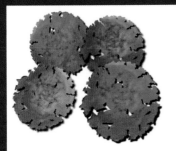

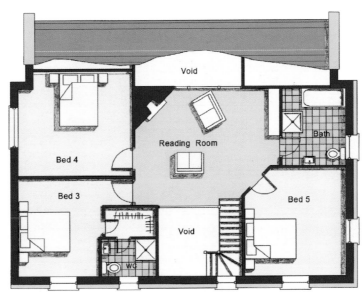

First Floor Plan

This 'traditional gothic' facade conceals a modern interior full of light. A winding stair greets the visitor at the door and leads to an impressive landing space. The landing room overlooks the living and dining areas as well as the entrance to the home. Large kitchen, dining and living rooms enhance the sense of space. The dining and living have velux windows above allowing light to flow in. 5 spacious bedrooms make this a comfortable family home, 2 of which have walk-in wardrobes and ensuites.

2049

Five Bedrooms.
Kitchen - 13' 01"x10' 10"
Dining - 14' 01"x14' 06"
Living - 12' 10"x17' 09"
Reading Rm - 18' 10"x14' 06"
Bed 1 -10' 05"x12' 02"
Bed 2 -10' 10"x17' 09"
Bed 3 - 10' 11"x12' 03"
Bed 4 - 14' 09"x13' 00"
Bed 5 - 13' 01"x13' 05"
Overall Length - 44' 09"
Overall Width - 36' 09"
Floor Area - 2250 sq. ft.

View from front garden towards porch entrance. Brick finish

2050

Four Bedrooms.
Kitchen - 13' 05''x18' 01''
Dining - 11' 06''x14' 09''
Living - 15' 09''x17' 10''
Sun Lounge - 11' 02''x12' 06''
Study - 10' 06''x12' 06''
Bed 1 -15' 09''x17' 09''
Bed 2 -11' 02''x19' 04''
Bed 3 - 13' 05''x14' 09''
Bed 4 - 10' 05''x13' 09''
Overall Length - 47' 03''
Overall Width - 50' 02''
Floor Area - 2922 sq. ft.

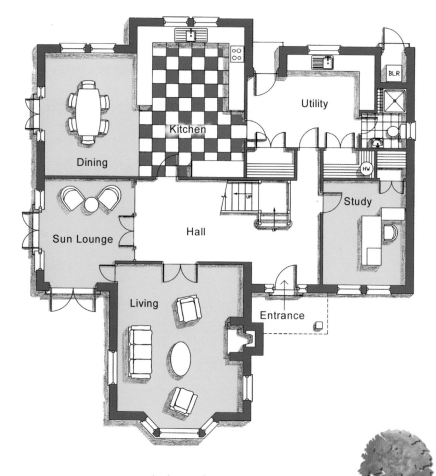

Ground Floor Plan

View towards rear of house. Render finish with timber windows and eaves

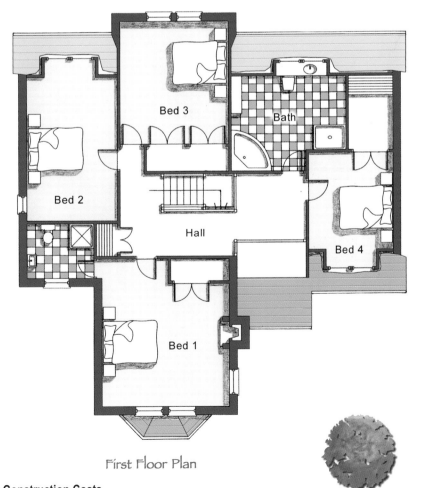

First Floor Plan

This large four bedroomed luxury house has been illustrated alternatively in brick (opposite) and render (above) and is suited to either finish.

The entrance leads into a large open hall with an exposed dog-leg leading up to the first floor.

The dining room and sun lounge would ideally face south-west with the wall between the sun lounge and hall being fully glazed to enable natural light to flood into the very heart of the house.

The large first floor bathroom is easily big enough to accommodate a corner bath.

For **Construction Costs**
See Pages 154 & 155

View from front garden towards house

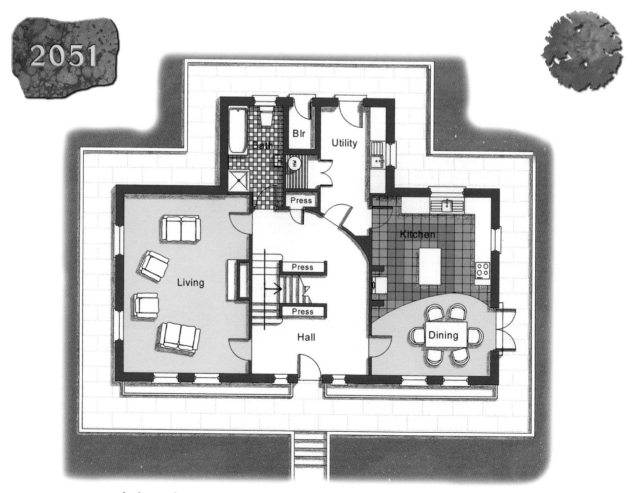

2051

Bath

Blr

Utility

Press

Living

Press

Kitchen

Press

Hall

Dining

Ground Floor Plan

134

Three Bedrooms.
Kitchen/Dining - 14' 01"x20' 08"
Living - 15' 01"x20' 08"
Bed 1 -14' 01"x15' 01"
Bed 2 -15' 01"x15' 01"
Bed 3 - 13' 03"x13' 02"
Overall Length - 46' 00"
Overall Width - 33' 00"
Floor Area - 1919 sq. ft.

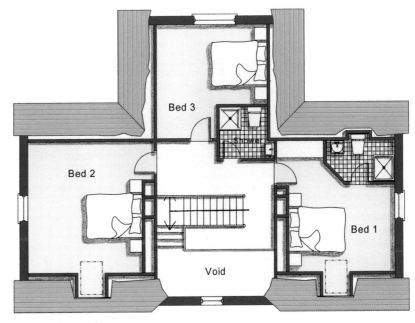

First Floor Plan

This storey and a half design has a homely elegance, delineated by a horizontal, raised plaster band.

Internally the large open hall and feature staircase wrap around two full height shelving recesses. Circulation flows around this central core giving easy access to all rooms. The first floor landing has a balcony which overlooks the entrance and gives visual connection.

Bedrooms 1 and 2 are shown on plan with velux windows to front, however, the main image (opposite) does not include them. Both bedrooms would benefit from the additional natural light provided by a velux.

View towards rear of house

For **Construction Costs**
See Pages 154 & 155

135

View towards front entrancee

2052

Six Bedrooms.
Kitchen - 12' 10''x11' 10''
Dining - 12' 02''x11' 10''
Living - 12' 10''x13' 09''
Sitting - 12' 10''x18' 08''
Bed 1 -12' 10''x12' 10''
Bed 2 -12' 10''x9' 10''
Bed 3 - 12' 10''x9' 02''
Bed 4 - 12' 10''x9' 02''
Bed 5 - 12' 10''x10' 10''
Bed 6 - 12' 10''x13' 09''
Overall Length - 41' 08''
Overall Width - 39' 06''
Floor Area - 2279 sq. ft.

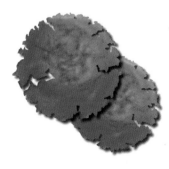

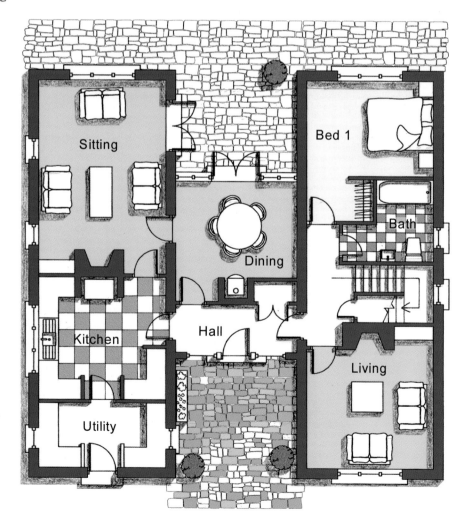

Ground Floor Plan

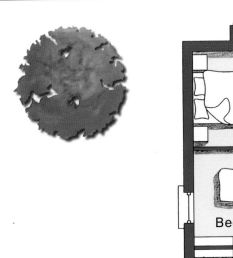

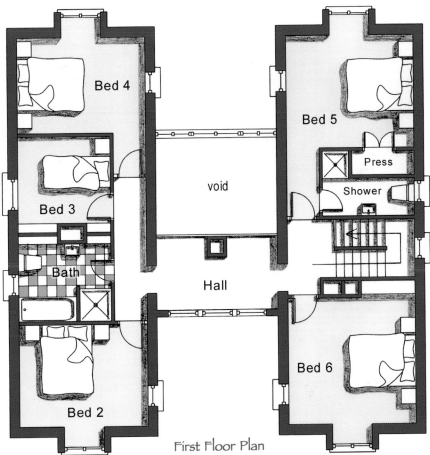

Bed 4

Bed 5

Bed 3

void

Press

Shower

Bath

Hall

Bed 2

Bed 6

First Floor Plan

This spacious family house offers a grand entrance, with public and private areas zoned to avoid intrusion. The Sitting and Dining rooms open onto a patio, enclosed on three sides. The Dining room is a double height space that opens onto the balcony above. This design provides privacy whilst allowing a public façade and an impressive entrance.

The central element has been illustrated with a copper roof which works well with the stone walls and timber windows. Alternative finishes may be considered.

View towards rear with dining room at centre

For Construction Costs
See Pages 154 & 155

View from front garden towards dining and living rooms

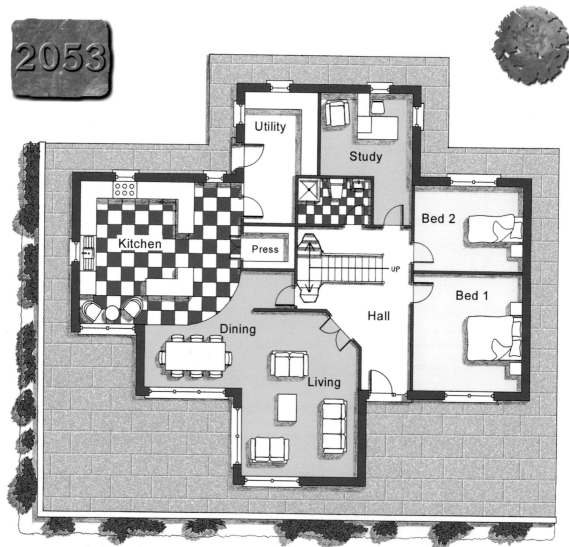

2053

Ground Floor Plan

Five Bedrooms.
Kitchen - 19' 04"x13' 01"
Dining - 11' 10"x10' 06"
Living - 14' 01"x19' 00"
Study - 11' 02"x9' 06"
Bed 1 -13' 01"x13' 05"
Bed 2 -13' 01"x9' 10"
Bed 3 - 13' 11"x14' 01"
Bed 4 - 12' 06"x11' 06"
Bed 5 - 13' 01"x14' 01"
Overall Length - 55' 05"
Overall Width - 46' 03"
Floor Area - 2639 sq. ft.

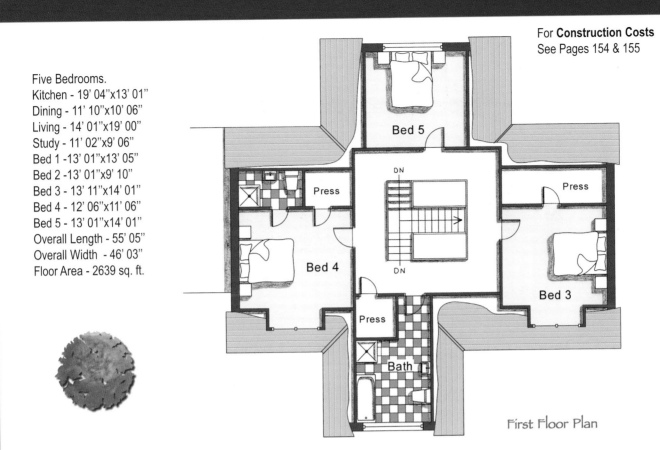

First Floor Plan

Here, a cruciform plan is generated from a central staircase with the south west corner of kitchen, dining and living open plan and opened up to natural light via the full height glazing which is unashamedly modern.

At first floor the rooms radiate out from the large open landing with voids looking down to the hall below.

Internal view from kitchen, through the dining area and into the living room

View from front garden towards porch entrance

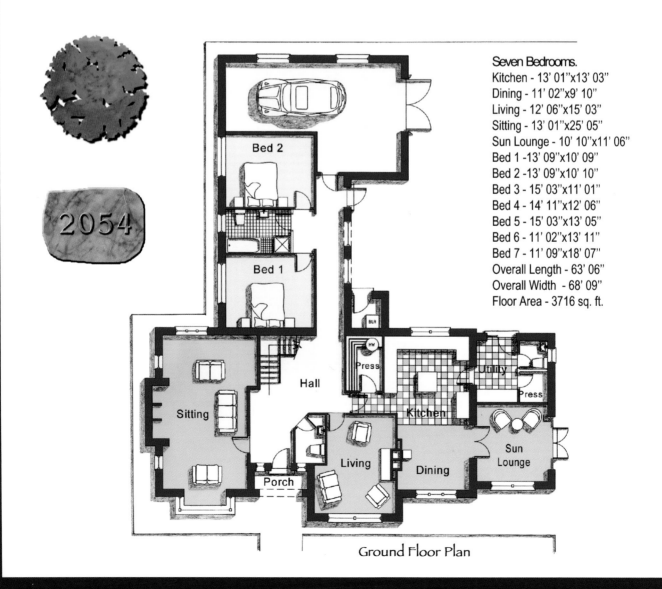

2054

Seven Bedrooms.
Kitchen - 13' 01"x13' 03"
Dining - 11' 02"x9' 10"
Living - 12' 06"x15' 03"
Sitting - 13' 01"x25' 05"
Sun Lounge - 10' 10"x11' 06"
Bed 1 -13' 09"x10' 09"
Bed 2 -13' 09"x10' 10"
Bed 3 - 15' 03"x11' 01"
Bed 4 - 14' 11"x12' 06"
Bed 5 - 15' 03"x13' 05"
Bed 6 - 11' 02"x13' 11"
Bed 7 - 11' 09"x18' 07"
Overall Length - 63' 06"
Overall Width - 68' 09"
Floor Area - 3716 sq. ft.

Ground Floor Plan

First Floor Plan

Bed 7

Press
Press

Bed 6

Press

Hall

Bed 5

Bed 4

Bed 3

Designed to maximise the benefits of a south facing site, this 7 bedroom house could easily be adapted to Bed & Breakfast use, allowing ideal separation between guest and owner accommodation. Although totalling over 3,700 sq. ft., the use of storey and a half and single storey sections, along with half hips and narrow roof spans all help to reduce the overall scale and impact of the dwelling.

Rear view

For **Construction Costs**
See Pages 154 & 155

Aerial view towards courtyard

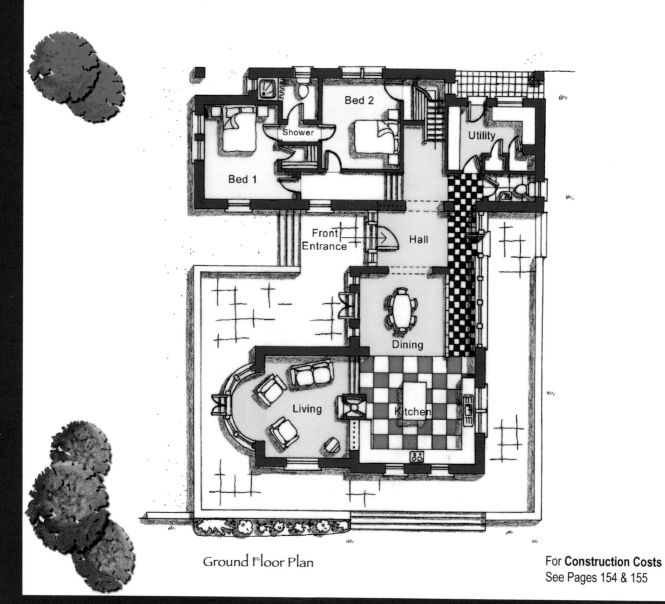

Ground Floor Plan

For **Construction Costs**
See Pages 154 & 155

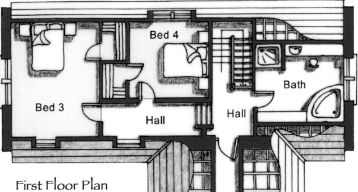
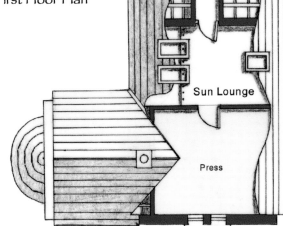

Bed 4

Bed 3

Hall

Hall

Bath

First Floor Plan

2055

Sun Lounge

Press

Four Bedrooms.
Kitchen - 17' 05"x13' 02"
Dining - 13' 02"x11' 06"
Living - 16' 05"x14' 05"
Sun Lounge - 11' 06"x11' 06"
Bed 1 - 11' 06"x13' 06"
Bed 2 -11' 10"x12' 10"
Bed 3 -13' 02"x17' 05"
Bed 4 -12' 06"x11' 10"
Overall Length - 51' 10"
Overall Width - 57' 09"
Floor Area - 2841 sq. ft.

This split-level design is planned around a central courtyard and produces a linear plan which benefits from dual aspect rooms and much natural light.

The living room, with its feature stone bay window, is open plan to the kitchen but visually separated by the central fireplace and split-level.
The first floor sun lounge is a sanctuary, a central place for quiet relaxation.

Rear view towards glazed hallway and utility room entrance

Front Perspective

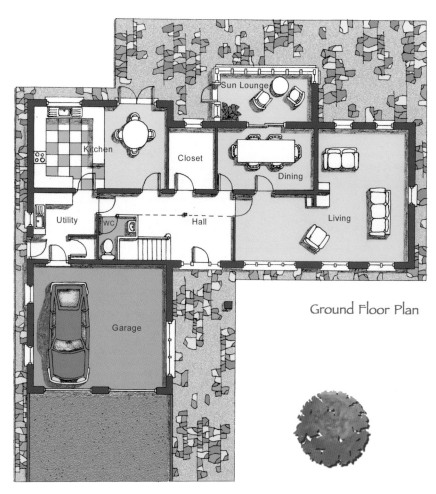

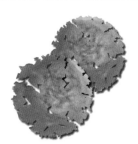

Sun Lounge

Kitchen

Closet

Dining

Utility

WC

Hall

Living

Garage

Ground Floor Plan

2056

Five Bedrooms.
Kitchen - 20' 04''x12' 06''
Dining - 14' 09''x9' 06''
Living - 19' 04''x13' 09''
Sun lounge - 10' 10''x20' 04''
Bed 1 -11' 06''x19' 04''
Bed 2 -10' 02''x14' 05''
Bed 3 -10' 02''x14' 05''
Bed 3 -10' 02''x12' 06''
Bed 3 -10' 02''x12' 06''
Play area - 9'10''x9' 10''
Overall Length - 58' 10''
Overall Width - 47' 06''
Floor Area - 3019 sq. ft.

For **Construction Costs**
See Pages 154 & 155

First Floor Plan

Bed 4   Bed 5

Landing

Void   Bed 1

WC

Bed 3   Bed 2

The double height entrance lobby adds strength to this delightful cottage style dwelling.

Despite having five bedrooms this house manages to maintain the scale of a cottage.

The combined double garage gives a defined gable frontage to compliment the decreasing eaves levels of the main body of the house.

The living room has a vaulted ceiling creating a large spacious area.

Rear perspective

Copyright 2000 Plan-A-Home

View from front garden towards south elevation

2057

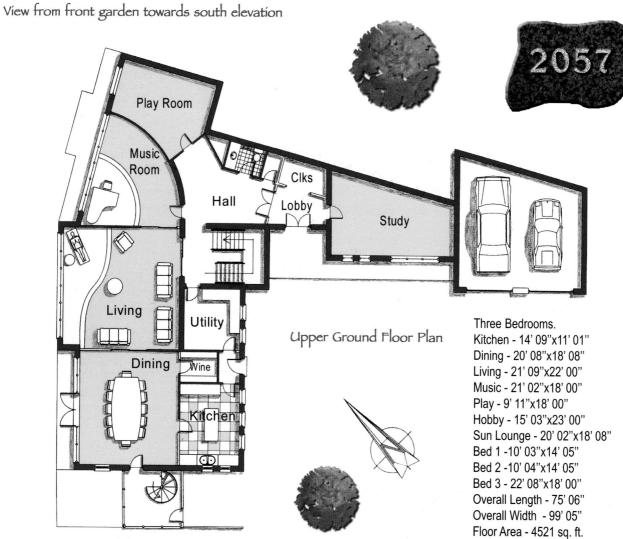

Play Room

Music Room

Clks

Hall

Lobby

Study

Living

Utility

Upper Ground Floor Plan

Dining

Wine

Kitchen

Three Bedrooms.
Kitchen - 14' 09"x11' 01"
Dining - 20' 08"x18' 08"
Living - 21' 09"x22' 00"
Music - 21' 02"x18' 00"
Play - 9' 11"x18' 00"
Hobby - 15' 03"x23' 00"
Sun Lounge - 20' 02"x18' 08"
Bed 1 -10' 03"x14' 05"
Bed 2 -10' 04"x14' 05"
Bed 3 - 22' 08"x18' 00"
Overall Length - 75' 06"
Overall Width - 99' 05"
Floor Area - 4521 sq. ft.

For **Construction Costs**
See Pages 154 & 155

This strikingly bold contemporary design incorporates many distinctive yet practical features from the grass roof, which acts both as an insulating blanket and roof garden to the large glazed areas, which can be used to maximize solar heat gain. Internally the dwelling is notable for the open plan arrangement of the entrance level made possible by the use of sliding partitions and for the generous proportions of the en-suite bedrooms which are located, unusually, below the reception rooms.

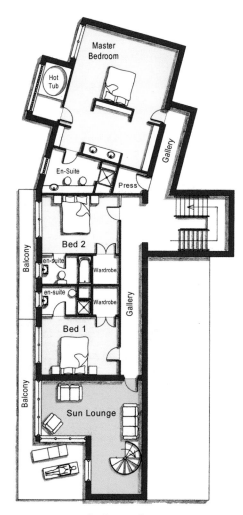

lower Ground Floor Plan

Aerial View towards entrance with garages to right

View from garden towards Sitting room entrance and study balcony

Four Bedrooms.
Kitchen/Dining - 14' 07"x18' 09"
Sitting - 16' 11"x19' 05"
Living - 13' 05"x13' 10"
Bed 1 -11' 10"x13' 02"
Bed 2 -10' 06"x10' 10"
Bed 3 - 10' 05"x12' 05"
Bed 4 - 9' 10"x13' 10"
Study - 16' 02"x8' 03"
Overall Length - 81' 00"
Overall Width - 30' 10"
Floor Area - 2358 sq. ft.

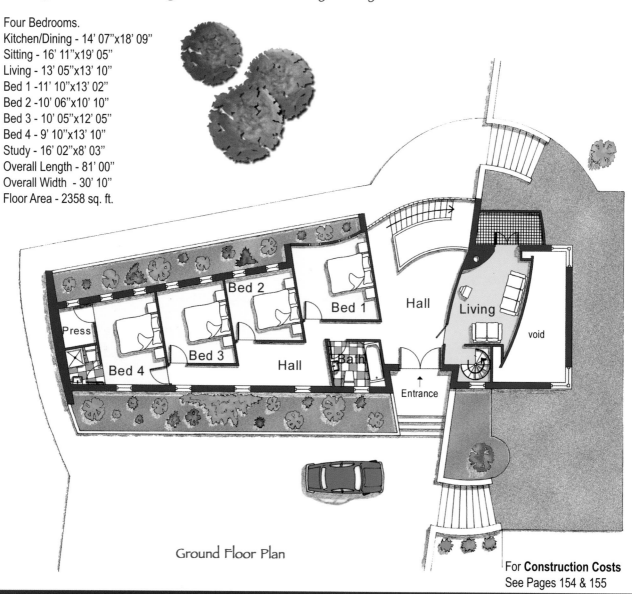

Ground Floor Plan

For **Construction Costs**
See Pages 154 & 155

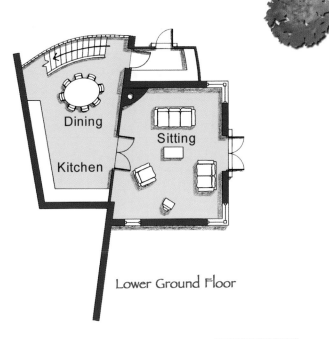

Dining

Sitting

Kitchen

Lower Ground Floor

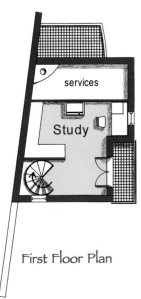

services

Study

First Floor Plan

2058

This design was arrived at with the more demanding site in mind. Essentially divided into two blocks separated by a glazed entrance hall; the building straddles sloping ground with ease.

The approach taken to the design of this house is un-ashamedly modern, whilst using natural materials to realise its goals. The bedroom block is deliberately kept quite separate from living areas which occupy three levels in a tall block located on lower ground. This house has been designed to be bright and airy opening itself out to it's surrounding landscape.

View from garden towards utility entrance and glass block wall (with stairs behind).

View from front garden towards porch entrance

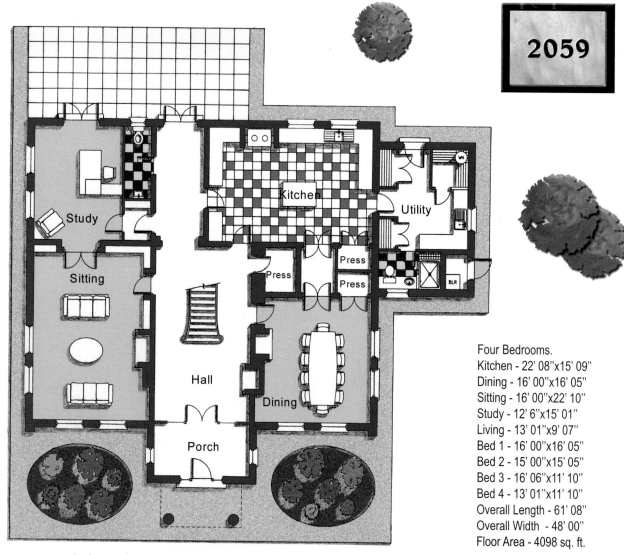

2059

Study

Sitting

Kitchen

Utility

Press

Press

Press

BLR

Hall

Dining

Porch

Four Bedrooms.
Kitchen - 22' 08"x15' 09"
Dining - 16' 00"x16' 05"
Sitting - 16' 00"x22' 10"
Study - 12' 6"x15' 01"
Living - 13' 01"x9' 07"
Bed 1 - 16' 00"x16' 05"
Bed 2 - 15' 00"x15' 05"
Bed 3 - 16' 06"x11' 10"
Bed 4 - 13' 01"x11' 10"
Overall Length - 61' 08"
Overall Width - 48' 00"
Floor Area - 4098 sq. ft.

Ground Floor Plan

For **Construction Costs**
See Pages 154 & 155

The elevation treatment to this house using plaster bands, window reveal moulds and a corbel eaves finish shows how a simple classical design can be dressed up without introducing expensive complicated roofs etc. All rooms are generous and practically arranged with features including a spacious hall, elegant double return stairs, extensive master bedroom with walk through wardrobe.

This design would still retain its character even if floor area and layout required reducing.

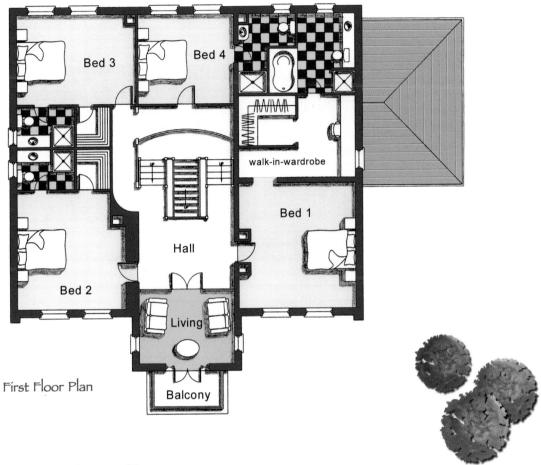

Bed 3

Bed 4

walk-in-wardrobe

Bed 1

Hall

Bed 2

Living

First Floor Plan

Balcony

View towards rear of house

View towards front of house

Five Bedrooms.
Kitchen/Dining - 25' 06"x15' 04"
Dining - 12' 06"x15' 05"
Drawing Room - 27' 11"x23' 00"
Gymnasium - 19' 08"x14' 10"
Games Room - 19' 08"x15' 07"
Master Bed -19' 08"x13' 08"
Bed 2 -12' 07"x15' 03"
Bed 3 -11' 10"x17' 10"
Bed 4 - 15' 11"x19' 04"
Bed 5 - 12' 05"x15' 06"
Overall Length - 74' 00"
Overall Width - 45' 02"
Floor Area - 4161 sq. ft.

2060

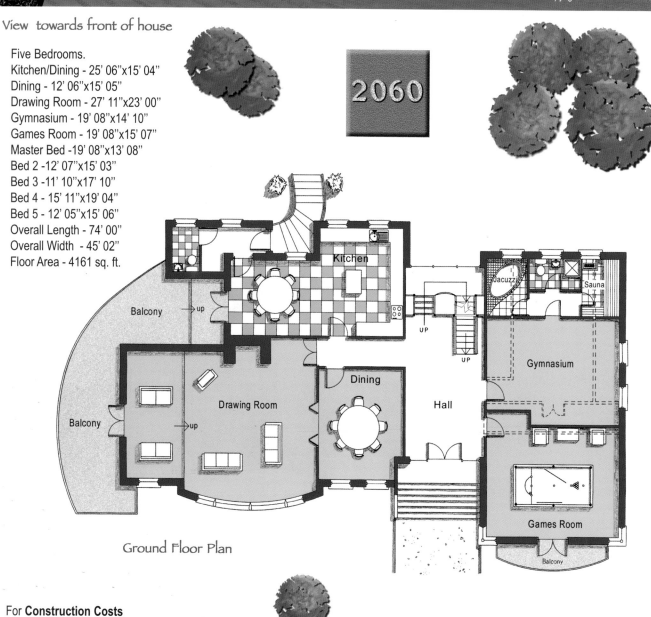

Ground Floor Plan

For Construction Costs
See Pages 154 & 155

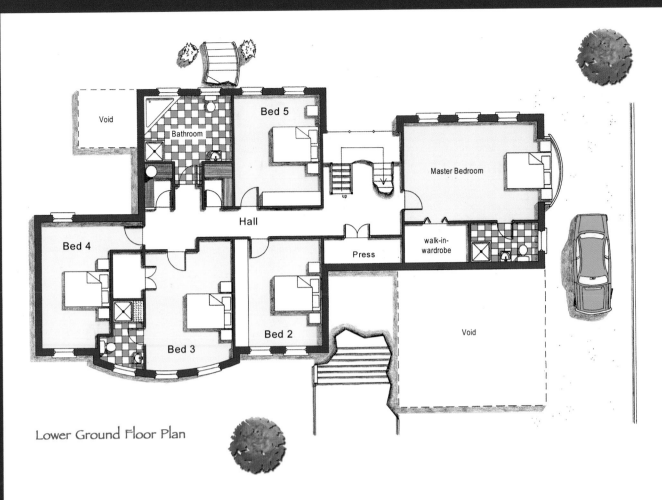

Lower Ground Floor Plan

This is a substantial house designed for those who lead active lives. To this end the building contains a games room together with gym and associated sauna, Jacuzzi and shower room. All living areas are located on the upper ground floor (maximising views in all directions) with bedroom areas below. These lower areas are cut into the site so as to further integrate the building with it's surrounding landscape. Living areas are planned to provide generous and elegant spaces making the best use of natural light. Although modern in design the building uses warm and natural materials, such as Scandinavian pine, stone, natural slate, plaster and cedar, to realise it's objectives.

View towards rear of house

Construction Costs

As building costs vary greatly throughout the country our intention is to indicate prices typical for general areas. If you are on the border of the highlighted regions your price will fall somewhere between those given. To help identify projected overall expenditure we have broken the prices into three stages.

Stage A - Main Structure

This includes for all works (material and labour) in Constructing your house: foundations, walls, roof, plastering, plumbing, electrical and joinery.
See Guideline Specifications on Page 155 for details.
Stone or brick finishes are shown on some houses for illustration purposes only. These finishes are **NOT** included in the guideline cost.
For brick cladding add approximately 10% to the Stage A amount.
For stone cladding add approximately 20% to the Stage A amount.

All costings are based on traditional construction methods (using cavity blockwork walls) and a contract procurement method - employing a contractor through selective tendering rather than utilising direct labour.
Guideline prices will also be reasonably accurate for timber frame construction as cost differences are negligible compared to traditional build.

Stage B - Fit Out

This section has deliberately been kept separate as you will probably want to control your own budget on these.
Items include:
Kitchen units
Utility units
Sanitaryware - as shown
Fireplaces-   as shown
Painting and decorating
Wall tiling – assume to ceiling height
Floor finishes – assume 25% of floor area covered
                          with ceramics and/or hardwood
Stairs-   Hardwood, where applicable
Patent roof glazing- Where applicable

Ranges, stoves and wardrobes, although shown, are not included.

The amount shown in Stage B includes Stages 'A' amounts.

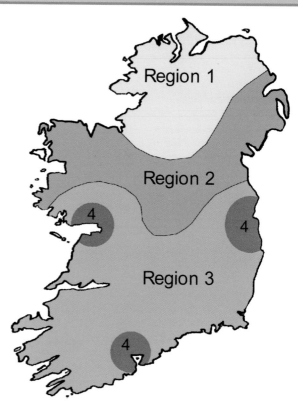

Region 1

Region 2

Region 3

NOTE: Region 4 (areas in red) - It is currently impossible to accurately predict pricing trends in these areas. However, developments in region 4 may increase by up to 10% to 20 % of region 3.
Other cities may also experience similar trends of escalating construction costs.

Stage C - Site Works

This is a provisional amount for all site works and services based on a green field site of approximately half an acre and is assumed to include for:
footpaths, tarmac driveways, sewerage, storm water and water supply.
Fencing or boundary walls have not been included in this amount.
A serviced site will be less expensive to develope.
The amounts shown in Stage C includes Stage 'B'.

SITE PURCHASE PRICE NOT INCLUDED

KEY

plan	stage	region 1	region 2	region 3
2031	A	142,491	158,877	176,689
	B	168,860	188,280	209,387
	C	184,518	205,738	228,803

To read costings:
1. Refer to plan number - for example 2031.
2. Find your region - e.g. Roscommon is Region 2.
3. The Chart indicates expenditure at Stages outlined i.e. Shell complete equals stage A = €158,877 but to complete house to a moving in stage = €205,738

Stage A

Roof :-   Tegral 2000 slates
External walls: Cavity, smooth rendered
Facia/soffit: uPVC or Aluminium.
Windows: uPVC, double glazed
External doors: uPVC, double glazed
Internal doors: 6 paneled hardwood\pine
Skirting/Arch.:   Hardwood
Heating/plumb.:   Conventional system with
                      rads and cylinder
Electrical: High standard of electrics.

Stage B

See previous page

Stage C

See previous page

design	stage	region 1	region 2	region 3
2031	A	142,491	158,877	176,689
	B	168,860	188,280	209,387
	C	184,518	205,738	228,803
2032	A	138,003	153,873	171,124
	B	163,511	182,315	202,754
	C	179,142	199,744	222,137
2033	A	156,094	174,046	193,557
	B	182,704	203,715	226,552
	C	201,442	224,608	249,789
2034	A	162,257	180,916	201,198
	B	189,854	211,688	235,420
	C	208,756	232,763	258,858
2035	A	148,388	165,484	184,000
	B	171,747	191,109	212,967
	C	201,359	224,516	249,686
2036	A	142,005	158,336	176,087
	B	172,561	192,407	213,977
	C	209,845	233,978	260,208
2037	A	129,641	144,539	160,754
	B	152,352	169,873	188,917
	C	168,930	188,357	209,473
2038	A	210,339	234,528	260,821
	B	250,550	279,363	310,683
	C	275,372	307,039	341,461
2039	A	144,008	160,570	178,570
	B	174,241	194,278	216,059
	C	195,236	217,689	242,093
2040	A	180,651	201,426	224,007
	B	210,555	234,768	261,088
	C	231,037	257,607	286,485
2041	A	171,373	191,081	212,503
	B	198,857	221,725	246,582
	C	217,432	242,437	269,616
2042	A	143,458	159,956	177,888
	B	167,286	186,523	207,434
	C	184,540	205,763	228,830
2043	A	213,636	238,205	264,909
	B	264,570	294,996	328,067
	C	285,031	317,809	353,437

Please Note:
The prices listed here are for guideline purposes only and are indicative of contract values current in €uro's at Summer 2006.

design	stage	region 1	region 2	region 3
2044	A	159,113	177,410	197,300
	B	187,649	209,228	232,685
	C	206,997	230,801	256,676
2045	A	191,798	213,856	237,831
	B	233,180	259,995	289,143
	C	257,659	287,291	319,499
2046	A	192,069	214,158	238,166
	B	245,814	274,082	304,809
	C	271,630	302,867	336,821
2047	A	200,951	224,060	249,180
	B	244,360	272,461	303,006
	C	260,796	290,788	323,387
2048	A	194,531	216,903	241,219
	B	228,861	255,179	283,787
	C	255,399	284,770	316,694
2049	A	141,882	158,198	175,933
	B	174,565	194,641	216,461
	C	194,112	216,435	240,699
2050	A	218,000	243,070	270,321
	B	254,902	284,216	316,079
	C	279,030	311,118	345,997
2051	A	132,042	147,228	163,732
	B	162,080	180,719	200,980
	C	179,277	199,893	222,302
2052	A	179,224	199,834	222,237
	B	209,846	233,978	260,209
	C	230,537	257,049	285,866
2053	A	203,030	226,379	251,757
	B	240,886	268,588	298,698
	C	264,413	294,821	327,873
2054	A	303,938	338,892	376,883
	B	350,698	391,028	434,865
	C	380,100	423,811	471,324
2055	A	238,329	265,737	295,527
	B	275,703	307,409	341,872
	C	301,973	336,701	374,447
2056	A	232,730	259,494	288,586
	B	274,469	306,033	340,342
	C	302,768	337,587	375,433
2057	A	419,488	467,728	520,165
	B	476,130	530,886	590,402
	C	515,945	575,279	639,771
2058	A	190,617	212,538	236,366
	B	226,754	252,830	281,175
	C	259,294	289,113	321,525
2059	A	324,431	361,740	402,294
	B	276,545	428,210	476,215
	C	423,382	472,071	524,993
2060	A	328,360	366,121	407,167
	B	401,271	447,417	497,576
	C	448,492	500,069	556,131

HMG
Associates
Architects

CMG
Architects

See inside back cover for office locations and details

WHO WE ARE

HMG Associates & CMG, Architects
Founded in 1980 we have since grown into a nationwide multi disciplinary practice with a network of offices in Letterkenny, Cork. Galway, Carlow and Moville.

Our success is driven by our determination and enthusiasm to deliver creative functional solutions to the highest standard on time and within budget

The company has extensive experience of a wide variety of projects both in private and public sectors of all scales and degrees of complexity.

Our style is one of listening and acting as the "hub" in forming a cohesive working partnership with clients, contractors, consultants and the needs of the built environment.

WHY HMG & CMG

Due to our multi disciplinary structure we provide you with a single point of reference for the various consultants required to develop and complete your project.

We advise and assist on all feasibility aspects of your proposal including viability, location, cost, business plan, loans, grant aid availability, etc., by carefully listening to and enthusiastically responding to your needs.

We can confidently assure you, through our team of experienced professionals that we have the necessary skills and procedures to achieve your goals from project inception through brief development, sketch and detailed design.

Plan-A-Home Publications

We also alter any plan in this publication to suit your needs and site requirements.

Arrange appointment in our nearest office for consultation & quotation"

HMG / CMG are the only practices with this franchise.

PLANNING PERMISSION
(Republic of Ireland)

After choosing your site, and having given some thought as to the nature of the development, the first stage is to apply for planning permission to the Planning Authority in your county, or to the Urban District Council, or in the case of cities, to the City Borough Corporation.

There are three types of planning application which can be made, i.e. outline, approval and full permission, and these are outlined below.

OUTLINE PERMISSION

In some cases, persons may wish to ascertain whether or not planning permission would be granted for a particular development/site. On the advice of your architect/engineer, it may be prudent to apply for outline permission to determine whether or not your development would be permitted. Outline permission allows you to make an application without going to the expense of preparing house plans.

An outline permission must be accompanied by:-
a) A complete application form.
b) A relevant fee.
c) Proposed site layout and location maps, showing location of proposed development on site, and giving brief description of same.
d) 2 copies of notice of application to Planning Authority inserted in local newspaper and 2 no. copies site notice.
Note:- Grant of outline permission does not permit carrying out of any works.

APPROVAL

Approval can only be sought where outline permission as described above, has already been granted, and must be accompanied by complete working drawings and specification, together with all documents as listed for outline permission.

FULL PERMISSION

Full permission is a combination of outline and approval as previously described and is a more direct and speedier method for sites where it is considered that planning permission should be relatively easy to obtain.
Details of complete documents required for planning applications, as follows:-
a) Complete application form, completed accurately, stating all details as requested.
b) Completed application Fee form, with remittance
c) 4 no. copies of plans, elevations, site maps, site location maps and 2 no. copies of newspaper notice, site notice and letter from Group Scheme if applicable.
d) Local Needs Form (applicable to some Counties)
e) A Soil Suitability/Permeability Test. Applicable to some sites.
Any other information considered relevent to your Application.

GENERAL PROCEDURE

Should the Planning Authority decide that insufficient information has been supplied they are entitled to request further information. Your application is then put on hold until the relevent information has been received, this should be supplied within four weeks. If the council are satisfied with your response they will issue their decision within 4-5 weeks. Planning approval is then given one month later.

PUBLIC NOTICE

This is done by means of notification in a locally distributed newspaper and also with a notice on site, placed in a convenient position so as to be ledgiblefrom main thoroughfare, and must remain in place for a period of one month of the application. 2 no. copies of each to be submitted with application for planning.

SITE LAYOUT MAPS

6 layout maps, clearly showing boundaries of the site, site entrance, storm and foul drainage details, water supply etc. A Letter of consent from any group schemes or landowners to right-of-ways must accompany the application. Proven site lines are also required to be shown on the map.

SITE LOCATION MAPS

6 no. site location maps, being extracts from Ordnance Survey sheets, and showing clearly the location of site and adjoining developments in relation to any churches, crossroads, towns or any other distinct landmark in the area. Outline of site to be marked in red and overall landowners holding outlined in blue.

HOUSE PLANS

6 no. copies of detailed plans and specifications, clearly illustrating layout, elevations, sections, details of finishes, and all materials to be used in the construction.

OBJECTION

Objection can be made in writing as follows:-
a) By the applicant to the An Bord Pleanála in relation to it's decision to refuse, or to object to some of the conditions relevant to the Grant of Permission. The applicant has four weeks from the date of receipt of a decision, within which to object.
b) Objections can be lodged by a third party against a planning application subject to previous submission of observations being made to planning authority with the first 5 weeks of application. Or alternatively by adjoining landowner/occupier who has been granted leave to appeal by the board.

This information is a simple guide. It is advisable to contact your local Planning Office who will be glad to assist you with full relevant information concerning your application. Most Local Authorities have adopted Development Plans for their Counties.
These documents should ascertain whether or not a Planning Application relating to your circumstances should succeed.

ORDER FORM

OR ORDER ON LINE WWW.PLAN-A-HOME.IE

**This form is to be used for direct ordering of unaltered plans.
(If you require plans to be altered please see page 5)**

FOR PLAN COSTS CALL 1890 222345 or 1850 222345
(00 353 74 9129651 outside Eire)

Design No.	

Planning Drawings (8 sets of plans)	€
Working Drawings (4 sets of plans & 4 sets of specification)	€
Reverse hand layout ₁100.00 extra.	€
Bill of quantities (Optional)	€
Total	€
Vat @ 21%	€
Total Due	€

Payment Details:

Cheque ☐   Postal Order ☐   Account No: _____

Credit Card ☐   Type ☐   Expiry Date: _____

Cardholders Signature:

Name: _____   Site Address: _____

Address: _____   _____

_____   _____

Tel. No: _____   e-mail: _____

Please post to:

**PLAN-A-HOME
Lower Main Street,
Letterkenny,
Co. Donegal.
Ireland.**

Other Items required for planning permission:

6 sets of site layout/location map.
2 copies of site notice.
2 copies of newspaper notice.
Fully completed application form.
Planning application fee.
Percolation test (dependent on Local Authority)
Local needs form (dependent on local authority)

Should you require any assistance with the above requirements contact any of the appointed Architectural offices listed inside the back cover.

Please complete your Specification list over leaf.

SPECIFICATION

Please tick the following to enable us to complete a detailed specification to suit your requirements (otherwise we will allow for a standard, good quality finish throughout).

Roof Covering:

| tiles | - concrete | ☐ | slates | - synthetic | ☐ | |
| | - clay | ☐ | | - natural | ☐ | other _____ |

Windows:

| hardwood | ☐ | uPVC | ☐ | aluminium | ☐ | other _____ |

External Doors\Frames:

| hardwood | ☐ | uPVC | ☐ | aluminium | ☐ | other _____ |

External Finish:

| dry dash | ☐ | smooth render | ☐ | brick (only if illustrated) | ☐ |
| wet dash | ☐ | | | stone (only if illustrated) | ☐ |

Fascia, Soffit, Barge:

| softwood | ☐ | aluminium | ☐ | |
| hardwood | ☐ | uPVC | ☐ | other _____ |

Second-fix-Joinery:

| sapelle doors | ☐ | hardwood panel doors | ☐ | |
| raised panel doors (regency) | ☐ | | other _____ |

Second-Fix-joinery Timbers:

| softwood | ☐ | MDF | ☐ | |
| hardwood | ☐ | | other _____ |

Garage Doors:

| hardwood | ☐ | roller shutter | ☐ | |
| overhead & insulated | ☐ | remote control | ☐ | other _____ |

Heating:

| oil | ☐ | electric | ☐ | geo thermal | ☐ |
| gas | ☐ | solid fuel | ☐ | underfloor | ☐ |